DRAMATIZED CLASSICS
for
RADIO-STYLE READING

Volume II

Other books by Lewy Olfson

RADIO PLAYS OF FAMOUS STORIES

RADIO PLAYS FROM SHAKESPEARE

DRAMATIZED CLASSICS FOR RADIO-STYLE READING
(VOLUME I)

Dramatized Classics

for

Radio-Style Reading

A collection of short plays
adapted from great literature
for royalty-free performance
or classroom reading

by LEWY OLFSON

Volume II

Publishers　　*Plays, Inc.*　　Boston

CAUTION

All material in this volume is fully protected by copyright law. All rights, including motion picture, recitation, television, public reading, radio broadcasting, and rights of translation into foreign languages, are strictly reserved.

.

NOTICE FOR AMATEUR PRODUCTION

These plays may be produced by schools, clubs, and similar amateur groups without payment of a royalty fee.

NOTICE FOR PROFESSIONAL PRODUCTION

For any form of non-amateur presentation (professional stage, radio or television), permission must be obtained in writing from the publisher. Inquiries should be addressed to PLAYS, INC., 8 Arlington Street, Boston 16, Massachusetts.

Library of Congress Catalog Card Number: 64-21325

MANUFACTURED IN THE UNITED STATES OF AMERICA

For

ANN, PAUL, *and* **MARK**

Contents

DRAMATIZED CLASSICS
for
RADIO-STYLE READING

Volume II

Washington Square

Washington Square

by Henry James

Characters

DR. SLOPER
CATHERINE SLOPER, *his daughter*
MRS. PENNIMAN, *his widowed sister*
MRS. ALMOND, *his married sister*
MARIAN ALMOND, *her daughter*
MORRIS TOWNSEND
GUEST
NARRATOR

MUSIC: *Gay waltz theme, in and under.*

GUEST: Such a lovely party, dear Mrs. Almond.

MRS. ALMOND: It is always a pleasure to have you, my dear.

GUEST: How gay all the young people are! And how elegant! I have been noticing in particular that very sweet girl sitting there in the corner. Who is she, pray?

MRS. ALMOND: Why, that is my niece, Catherine Sloper—my brother Austin's daughter.

GUEST: Ah! So that is Catherine Sloper of Washington Square—the heiress to the fabulous fortune!

MUSIC: *Out.*

NARRATOR: Catherine Sloper . . . the shy and sweet girl

from New York, the wealthy young woman of society, and the unhappy heroine of Henry James' great novel, *Washington Square*.

MUSIC: *Romantic theme, up full and out.*

NARRATOR: Dr. Austin Sloper, intelligent, handsome and wealthy member of New York society, is determined that his only child, Catherine, shall grow up to be a credit to him, to herself and to the Sloper family name. His wife dies, and Dr. Sloper raises the motherless little girl himself until she is ten years old, when it becomes apparent to him that the girl is neither pretty nor gifted. Feeling that the dull, plain child will benefit from the guidance of an older woman, Dr. Sloper invites his widowed sister, Lavinia Penniman, to live with them in Washington Square, and to take over the task of raising young Catherine.

DR. SLOPER: Try to make a clever woman of her, Lavinia. I should like her to be a clever woman.

MRS. PENNIMAN: My dear brother Austin, do you think it is better to be clever than good?

DR. SLOPER: Good for what, Lavinia? You are good for nothing unless you are clever!

MRS. PENNIMAN: Brother!

DR. SLOPER: Of course I wish Catherine to be good, but she won't be any the less virtuous for not being a fool. I am not afraid of her being wicked; she will never have the salt of malice in her character. I know my daughter, Lavinia; she is a plain and dull child. She is, as the French say, as good as good bread. But six years hence, I don't want to have to compare her to good bread and butter.

MRS. PENNIMAN (*With a slight laugh*): Are you afraid she

will turn insipid? My dear brother, it is I who supply the butter, so you needn't worry!

MUSIC: *Light theme, in, under, and out.*

NARRATOR: And so the further education of young Catherine Sloper is begun. Dr. Sloper thinks his sister rather a fool. But as his opinion of his child is not more flattering, he feels little harm can come of the relationship.

DR. SLOPER (*Thinking aloud*): When Catherine is about seventeen, Lavinia will try to persuade her that some young man with a mustache is in love with her. It will be quite untrue; no young man, with a mustache or without, will ever be in love with Catherine. Ah, it's a very good thing that poor Catherine isn't romantic!

NARRATOR: Time passes neither slowly nor quickly for the young girl and her widowed aunt at Washington Square, and when Catherine is sixteen, she is little changed from the girl she was at ten. During her sixteenth year, Catherine is invited to a dinner dance at the home of her married aunt, Mrs. Almond. It is the first party she has ever been to, and though her calm demeanor almost hides it, she is, for all her plainness, as excited as *any* young girl at her first dance. Shortly after she and Mrs. Penniman arrive at the party, one of the young ladies of the house, Catherine's pretty cousin Marian, introduces her to a handsome young gentleman.

SOUND: *Waltz music and noise of party guests, softly in background.*

MARIAN: Catherine, dearest cousin, how nice of you to come! And Aunt Lavinia! Morris, this is my young cousin, Catherine Sloper. Isn't she charming?

MORRIS (*Suavely*): I am delighted, Miss Sloper.

MARIAN: Do be a good boy, Morris, and dance with Catherine. She hasn't had a partner yet, and she's such a sweet girl! (*Fading*) Do excuse me, cousin. I must greet my other guests!

MORRIS (*In close*): May I have the pleasure of this dance, Miss Sloper?

MUSIC: *Romantic waltz, up from background, then under and out.*

NARRATOR: And off glides young Catherine on the arm of this handsome gentleman, while Mrs. Penniman beams her shining approval upon them. The young man asks Catherine for the following waltz, and then for the polka. Scarcely aware that she has never danced before in her life, the young girl feels herself flying in a golden dream. After the polka, Marian draws the girl aside.

MARIAN (*Gayly*): I needn't ask you, Catherine, what you think of Morris Townsend!

CATHERINE (*Calmly*): Is that his name?

MARIAN: I don't ask you what you think of his name, Catherine, but what you think of him.

CATHERINE: Oh, nothing particular.

MARIAN (*Laughing*): I have half a mind to tell him that! It will do him good. He's so terribly conceited.

CATHERINE (*Imploringly*): Oh, please don't tell him!

MARIAN: Don't tell him he's conceited? I have told him so a dozen times! (*Pause*) Why, Cousin Catherine! I do believe you're blushing.

MUSIC: *Happy theme, under and out.*

NARRATOR: On the way home from the party in the doctor's carriage, Dr. Sloper, Catherine and Mrs. Penniman relax from the excitement.

DR. SLOPER: Is it possible that this magnificent person is my child?

CATHERINE: I am not magnificent, Father.

DR. SLOPER: On the contrary, Catherine. Your dress is sumptuous, opulent, expensive. You look as if you had eighty thousand dollars a year.

CATHERINE (*Meekly*): Well, so long as I haven't. . . .

DR. SLOPER: So long as you haven't, you shouldn't look as if you had. Have you enjoyed the party?

CATHERINE: I—I am rather tired, Father.

DR. SLOPER: Ah, well. Tell me, Lavinia, who was that young man who was making love to you?

MRS. PENNIMAN (*Laughing*): Oh, my good brother!

DR. SLOPER: He seemed uncommonly tender. Whenever I looked at you, he had the most devoted air.

MRS. PENNIMAN: The devotion was not to me. It was to Catherine. He talked to me of her.

CATHERINE (*Faintly*): Oh, Aunt Lavinia!

MRS. PENNIMAN: He is very handsome. He is very clever. He has a rare felicity of expression.

DR. SLOPER: He is in love with this regal creature, my daughter, then?

CATHERINE (*More faintly*): Father!

MRS. PENNIMAN: I don't know about that. But he did admire her dress.

DR. SLOPER: You see, Catherine? *He* thinks you have eighty thousand a year.

MRS. PENNIMAN: I don't believe he thinks of that, brother. He is too refined.

DR. SLOPER: He must be tremendously refined not to think of that!

CATHERINE (*Blurting out*): Well, he is!

DR. SLOPER: What is the gentleman's name?

MRS. PENNIMAN: I didn't catch it, and I didn't like to ask

him. He asked to be introduced to me, but you know how indistinctly Cousin Jefferson always speaks. Catherine, dear, what was the gentleman's name?

CATHERINE (*After a slight pause, very evenly*): I don't know, Aunt Lavinia.

NARRATOR: A few days after the party, Morris Townsend comes to call at Washington Square. Dr. Sloper is out at the time, but when he returns to the house that night, Mrs. Penniman greets him with the information.

MRS. PENNIMAN: He has just left, Austin; it's such a pity you missed him.

DR. SLOPER: Whom in the world have I missed, Lavinia?

MRS. PENNIMAN: Mr. Morris Townsend. He has paid us such a delightful visit!

DR. SLOPER: And who in the world is Mr. Morris Townsend?

CATHERINE: Aunt Lavinia means the gentleman—the gentleman whose name I couldn't remember.

MRS. PENNIMAN: You know, Austin, the gentleman at the Almonds' party who was so struck with Catherine.

DR. SLOPER: Oh, his name is Morris Townsend, is it? And did he come here to propose to you?

CATHERINE (*Faintly*): Oh, Father!

MRS. PENNIMAN: I hope he won't do that without your permission, Austin.

DR. SLOPER: He seems to have yours already, Lavinia.

NARRATOR: The visits of Mr. Townsend become more numerous as the weeks roll by. At first, Dr. Sloper takes the whole matter as a joke, always asking his daughter the same question when the young man has left the house:

DR. SLOPER: Well, my dear, did he propose to you today?

NARRATOR: To which the poor plain girl always gives the same reply:

CATHERINE: Not today, Father. Perhaps he will do it next time.

NARRATOR: After a while, however, Dr. Sloper realizes the seriousness of his daughter's relationship with the young man, and he seeks information about him from Mrs. Almond, his married sister, at whose home Catherine first met Mr. Townsend.

MRS. ALMOND: Morris Townsend is a cousin of Marian's fiancé, Arthur Townsend. The name is the same, but I understand there are Townsends and Townsends. They talk of the family as having branches, as though it were a royal house. Arthur, it appears, is of the reigning line, but poor Catherine's young man is not.

DR. SLOPER: What of his immediate family? Who are his relations?

MRS. ALMOND: Only an older, widowed sister with several children—a Mrs. Montgomery. It is with her that he makes his home.

DR. SLOPER: What does this Mrs. Montgomery say about Morris Townsend?

MRS. ALMOND: That he has talents by which he might distinguish himself.

DR. SLOPER: Only he is lazy, eh?

MRS. ALMOND: She doesn't say that.

DR. SLOPER: That is family pride. What is his profession?

MRS. ALMOND: He doesn't have one. He is looking for something. I believe he was once in the Navy.

DR. SLOPER: Once? What is his age?

MRS. ALMOND: I suppose he is upwards of thirty.

DR. SLOPER: Do you think he is in earnest about Catherine?

MRS. ALMOND: I don't see why you should be incredulous. It seems to me that you have never done Catherine justice. You must remember that she has the prospect of thirty thousand a year.

DR. SLOPER: You at least appreciate her.

MRS. ALMOND: I don't mean that is her only merit; I simply mean that it is a great one. A great many young men think so too. You always have a way of implying Catherine is unmarriageable. But she does very well. She has a style of her own. And she is entitled to her share of happiness.

DR. SLOPER (*Darkly*): It is exactly her happiness that I am concerned with. Thank you for the information about Morris Townsend.

MRS. ALMOND: Take care what you do, Austin. Catherine is in love.

DR. SLOPER (*Slowly*): If that is the case, she must get over it.

MUSIC: *Mournful theme, in, under and out.*

NARRATOR: Yet the visits of Mr. Townsend to the young Miss Sloper of Washington Square continue. Three, four, five afternoons a week find the young couple together deep in conversation. To Dr. Sloper, the young man is absurd.

DR. SLOPER: He's a scoundrel, that's as clear as can be. A charming, highly polished scoundrel, grabbing after poor Catherine's fortune.

NARRATOR: To Mrs. Penniman, the young man is a delight.

MRS. PENNIMAN: Such grace! Such manners! Such charm!

NARRATOR: To Catherine, he is a dream come true.

CATHERINE: Be of good cheer, my dear Morris. If you can only be patient, you will win my father's good will.

NARRATOR: And the young man in question, Morris Townsend—how do the members of the Sloper family appear to him?

MORRIS (*Coolly*): The aunt, Mrs. Penniman, is a fool. The daughter, Catherine, is a sweet stupid thing. And the father—ah, yes, Dr. Sloper, the father. He is a shrewd, cold and cunning man.

NARRATOR: At last matters come to a head, and Morris proposes to Catherine.

MORRIS: Dear Catherine—my heart—you know that I adore you, that you are my entire world. Say you will be my wife!

CATHERINE: Dear Morris, we must do our duty. We must speak to my father. I will do it tonight. You must do it tomorrow.

MORRIS: It is very good of you to do it first. The young man generally does that. You will need all your powers of persuasion. But, after all, you're irresistible.

CATHERINE: Promise me this: tomorrow, when you talk with Father, you will be very gentle and respectful.

MORRIS: As much so as possible. It won't be any use, but I shall try. You must be prepared for bitterness, Catherine, and cruelty.

CATHERINE: My father is never cruel.

MORRIS: He will tell you I am after your money.

CATHERINE: And I shall simply tell him he is mistaken. Morris, are you very sure you love me?

MORRIS: My own dearest, can you doubt it?

CATHERINE: I have known it only a little while, but now it seems to me that I could never do without your love.

MORRIS: You will never be called upon to try. Tell me that if your father is dead against me, if he forbids our marriage, you will still be faithful. You are your own mistress; you are of age.

CATHERINE: Ah, Morris!

MUSIC: *Romantic theme, up full and out.*

NARRATOR: That evening, Catherine keeps her interview with her father.

CATHERINE: I have something to say to you, Father.

DR. SLOPER: I shall be happy to hear it, Catherine.

CATHERINE: I—Mr. Morris Townsend and I are engaged to be married.

DR. SLOPER: I see. You have moved quickly, Catherine.

CATHERINE: Yes, I think we have.

DR. SLOPER: You know I do not like the man.

CATHERINE: I think Morris—little by little—might persuade you to like him.

DR. SLOPER: I shall never let him speak to me again. I dislike him too much. I ask you to give him up, Catherine. He is a vicious man.

CATHERINE: Father!

DR. SLOPER: Don't you think I know something of men: their vices, their follies, their deceits? Do you not wish to make me happy?

CATHERINE: I should like to—but I am afraid I cannot. I shall tell Morris that we must wait.

DR. SLOPER: Wait? Wait for what?

CATHERINE: We must wait for your consent.

DR. SLOPER: Don't tell him any such nonsense as that. I know him well enough, and I shall never consent.

CATHERINE: We can wait a long time.

DR. SLOPER: Of course you can wait till I die if you like. Your engagement will have one delightful effect on you —it will make you extremely impatient for that event.

CATHERINE: I would rather not marry, if that were true.

DR. SLOPER: Give me proof of it then. Unless you break your engagement to Morris Townsend, I will assume you simply are waiting for my death.

CATHERINE: If I do not marry before your death, I will not marry after.

DR. SLOPER: If you don't wait for my death, you might as well marry immediately; there is nothing else to wait for. But you may tell Mr. Townsend this: if you marry without my consent, I won't leave you a cent of money. That will interest him more than anything else.

CATHERINE: That would be very right. I ought not to have any of your money in that case.

DR. SLOPER: Your simplicity, Catherine, is touching. Make that remark to Mr. Townsend and take a note of his answer. It won't be polite.

CATHERINE: He will never be impolite to me.

DR. SLOPER: Tell him what I say, all the same. And remember that if you see him, you will be an ungrateful child, cruel and without heart; you will have given your old father the greatest pain in his life.

CATHERINE: I shall think of what you have said. (*Fading*) Good night, Father.

DR. SLOPER (*Slowly*): Good night, Catherine.

NARRATOR: That night, Catherine writes a letter to Morris

telling him of what has passed between her father and herself.

CATHERINE: So you can see, dear Morris, that Father is completely against us. He has made it quite clear to me that if we marry, I shall be disinherited. Oh, it is a hard thing to be a good daughter and a faithful fiancée, both at the same time. What are we to do? I dare not ask you to visit me. Write me, instead, and send me your good advice. (*Fading*) With all my dearest love. . . .

MORRIS (*Cross-fading on*): How deep your grief must be. Do not for a moment think that I urge you to wait before marrying me, for the money's sake. Without a farthing, you come to me rich; in you is my fortune. But as I know your father cannot help but relent, how much wiser it would be if we were to wait before marrying. It would mean not only the fortune, then, but what is far more important—your father's blessing. (*Fading.*) Be true, my love.

NARRATOR: After the dreadful interview with Dr. Sloper, Catherine makes no reference whatever to Morris Townsend, but continues her life as a quiet, dutiful child. Months roll by, and the two lovers do not see each other, contenting themselves with poor little letters. Much to his surprise, Dr. Sloper realizes that Catherine is not submitting to his will, but merely marking time. After a year's time, he is hardly shocked, one day, to hear Catherine say:

CATHERINE: I think we shall marry soon, Father.

DR. SLOPER: Why do you tell me that? It's no concern of mine.

CATHERINE: Oh, Father! Don't you care, even if you do feel so?

DR. SLOPER: Not a button. Once you marry, it's quite the same to me when or where or why you do it; and if you think to compound your folly by hoisting your flag in this way, you may spare yourself the trouble. Why do you delay in consummating this wickedness?

CATHERINE: It is not easy for us to make up our minds.

DR. SLOPER: Put it off, then, for six months, and in the meantime I will take you to Europe. I should like you very much to go.

CATHERINE: Oh, Father, it would be delightful to go to Europe.

DR. SLOPER: Very well, then. We will go. You must begin to pack your clothes.

CATHERINE: I had better tell Mr. Townsend.

DR. SLOPER: If you mean that you had better ask his leave, I hope he will give it!

NARRATOR: It is obvious to Mrs. Penniman that her brother hopes Catherine will forget Townsend on the European tour; and as she is very fond of her niece's lover, she makes her views plain to Catherine.

MRS. PENNIMAN: He thinks it will make you forget Morris, my dear. That is why your father wants to take you to Europe.

CATHERINE: Oh?

MRS. PENNIMAN: "Out of sight, out of mind," you know.

CATHERINE: If he thinks that, I ought to tell him beforehand it will do no good.

MRS. PENNIMAN: Tell him afterwards, my dear! After he has had all the trouble and expense! That's the way to serve him!

MUSIC: *Active theme, up full and out.*

NARRATOR: And so Doctor Sloper and his daughter sail

for Europe. If the Doctor has hoped that Catherine will forget Mr. Townsend while she is abroad, he is mistaken. And just as she does not retreat from her position, he does not retreat from his. The day before leaving Europe for New York, Dr. Sloper turns to Catherine and says:

DR. SLOPER: What do you mean to do when you get home?

CATHERINE: Do you mean about Mr. Townsend? We shall probably marry.

DR. SLOPER: Do you hear from him as much as ever?

CATHERINE: Yes; twice a month.

DR. SLOPER: And does he always talk about marriage?

CATHERINE: Oh, yes! That is, he talks about other things, too, but he always says something about that.

DR. SLOPER: I am glad to hear he varies his subjects; his letters might otherwise be monotonous.

CATHERINE: He writes beautifully.

DR. SLOPER: They always write beautifully. However, in a given case, that doesn't diminish the merit. So, as soon as you arrive, you are going off with him?

CATHERINE: I cannot tell you till we arrive.

DR. SLOPER: That's reasonable enough. All I ask of you is that you *do* tell me, that you give me definite notice. When a poor man is to lose his only child, he likes to have an inkling of it beforehand.

CATHERINE: Oh, Father, you will not lose me!

DR. SLOPER: Three days before will do, if you are in a position to be positive then. He ought to be very thankful to me, do you know, in that I have fattened the sheep for him before he kills it, by taking you abroad and adding to your knowledge and worth. Go to bed, and get a good night's sleep. We shall probably have a most uncomfortable voyage.

NARRATOR: Once back in Washington Square, Catherine does not choose to anger her father further by inviting Morris to come to see her at home. Instead, she sends her Aunt Lavinia to bring Morris news of the situation.

MORRIS: I am very grateful to you, Mrs. Penniman, for bringing this news of Catherine. So this is how things stand. He will never give us a penny! Well, well. A man must know when he is beaten. I must give her up.

MRS. PENNIMAN (*Quietly*): I think I understand you.

MORRIS (*Harshly*): I certainly say it distinctly enough— brutally and vulgarly enough! I must give her up! (*Softening*) I say, couldn't you prepare her a bit for it? Try to make the break easier?

MRS. PENNIMAN: My poor Morris, do you know how much she loves you?

MORRIS: No, I don't. I don't want to know. I have always tried to keep from knowing. It would be too painful.

MRS. PENNIMAN: She will suffer much.

MORRIS: You must console her. If you are as good a friend to me as you pretend to be, you will manage it.

MRS. PENNIMAN: You talk of my pretending to like you; but I can't pretend to hate you. I can only tell her I think very highly of you; and how will that console her for losing you?

MORRIS: The doctor will help you. He will be delighted, and he will invent some way of comforting her.

MRS. PENNIMAN: He will invent a new torture for her! Heaven deliver her from her father's comfort! It will consist of his crowing over her and saying "I told you so" till the end of his days.

MORRIS: I hope you will console her more than you are consoling me!

MRS. PENNIMAN: I will be your friend for life!

MORRIS: Never mind my life, Mrs. Penniman. Be my friend *now!*

NARRATOR: Much to her credit, Mrs. Penniman carries out Morris' mission as delicately as possible. Instead of telling Catherine the truth, she tells the girl that Morris has been called away from New York quite suddenly, but that he will return. As days roll into weeks and weeks into months, the truth slowly dawns upon the girl. Poor Catherine! How deep a wound in her heart is made by her lover's faithless desertion is known to none, for she keeps her sorrow hidden.

MRS. PENNIMAN: Dear Catherine, you can trust in me.

CATHERINE (*Calmly*): What am I to trust you with?

MRS. PENNIMAN: With your secret—your sorrow.

CATHERINE: I have no sorrow.

MRS. PENNIMAN: My poor child, you can't deceive me. I know everything. Take comfort in this thought, my dear. It is better as it is.

NARRATOR: If Mrs. Penniman is kind, Dr. Sloper is cruel. He suspects the truth of the matter, but cannot be content until he has tasted the full flavor of his victory.

DR. SLOPER: You seem to have forgotten, Catherine, the promise you made to me in England. It would be a convenience to me to know when I may expect to have an empty house. When are you going? Is it tomorrow? Is it next week, or the week after?

CATHERINE (*Calmly*): I shall not be going away, Father.

DR. SLOPER: What? Has your paragon of virtue deserted you?

CATHERINE (*Slowly*): I have broken off my engagement.

DR. SLOPER: Broken it off, eh?

CATHERINE: I have asked him to leave New York, and he has gone away for a long time.

DR. SLOPER: How does he take his dismissal?

CATHERINE: I don't know.

DR. SLOPER: You mean you don't care? You are rather cruel, after encouraging him and playing with him so long.

NARRATOR: And so the name of Morris Townsend is dropped from the conversation in the house at Washington Square, and life moves on, year after year. One day, when the doctor has become quite an old man, he says to Catherine:

DR. SLOPER: I should like you to promise me something before I die, Catherine. Promise me not to marry Morris Townsend after I am gone.

CATHERINE: Why do you mention him after all these years, Father?

DR. SLOPER: I understand he is in New York again. Will you promise?

CATHERINE: I don't think you understand, Father. I seldom think of Mr. Townsend.

DR. SLOPER: It will be easy, then, to continue so. Promise me, after my death, to do the same. I ask you for a particular reason. I am altering my will.

CATHERINE: I am sorry, Father, but I cannot promise.

DR. SLOPER: Please explain, then.

CATHERINE: I can't explain, and I can't promise.

DR. SLOPER: Very well, then. My will must be changed. Upon my word, Catherine, I had no idea how obstinate you are!

NARRATOR: Within the year, Dr. Sloper died, his fortune divided among several hospitals and charitable institutions. Shortly after the funeral, a middle-aged gentleman presents himself at the house in Washington Square, and asks to speak with Miss Sloper.

CATHERINE: What is it, Aunt Lavinia?

MRS. PENNIMAN: There is—there is someone to see you, Catherine. An old friend of yours, who wishes to pay his respects.

CATHERINE: Oh? Who is the person?

MRS. PENNIMAN: Mr. Morris Townsend.

CATHERINE: I see. Tell Mr. Townsend that I am not in.

MRS. PENNIMAN: But, Catherine—will you not even greet him?

CATHERINE: I am not in, Aunt Lavinia, nor will I ever be to Mr. Morris Townsend.

MRS. PENNIMAN (*Fading slightly*): But, Catherine . . .

CATHERINE (*Slowly*): I am going to my room, Aunt Lavinia. I bid you good night.

MRS. PENNIMAN (*Calling, from off mike*): He hopes you can be friends, Catherine!

CATHERINE: Tell Mr. Townsend it was unnecessary for him to come in that hope. (*Firmly*) Good night, Aunt Lavinia.

MUSIC: *Mournful theme, full to finish.*

THE END

Don Quixote

Don Quixote

by Miguel de Cervantes

Characters

DON QUIXOTE	BENEDICTINE FRIAR
TWO VILLAGERS	TRAVELING LADY
QUIXOTE'S NIECE	THREE PRISONERS
CURATE	GUARD
SANCHO PANZA	NARRATOR
TERESA, *his wife*	

DON QUIXOTE (*With a proud flourish*): I challenge thee in the name of Dulcinea del Toboso!

MUSIC: *Light theme.*

NARRATOR: One of the most famous of all fictional characters is the noble knight-errant created by the Spanish writer, Miguel de Cervantes. This knight gave his heart to the accomplishment of impossible tasks; he gave his mind to the pursuit of justice and truth; and he gave his name to all noble and lost causes. Ladies and gentlemen, here is the story of one of literature's most sterling heroes, Don Quixote of La Mancha.

MUSIC: *Rollicking theme.*

NARRATOR: In La Mancha, one of the provinces of Spain, lives Don Quixote, a gangling, gawky, gregarious scholar

23

of fifty years. Bald-headed, bowlegged, near-sighted and spindle-shanked, poor old Don Quixote is the laughing-stock of the village. Everyone knows him; everyone likes him; and everyone laughs at him.

1ST VILLAGER (*Fading on*): There goes old Don Quixote, with his nose in a book, as usual.

2ND VILLAGER: The doddering simpleton! How does his niece put up with him?

1ST VILLAGER: Oh, he doesn't do any harm. And he certainly means well enough.

2ND VILLAGER: Aye, he *means* well. But look at the trouble he's always getting himself into! Always reading books, always studying, muddling everything he learns until it's back side to and upside down and inside out! He doesn't live in our world. He lives in a world of his own! The days of chivalry and knight-errantry have long since died on earth, but they live yet in the mind of Don Quixote.

1ST VILLAGER: Oh, let the old codger alone. What harm does he do anyone? Let poor old Don Quixote stay in his dream world of make-believe!

MUSIC: *Bright theme.*

NARRATOR: "His dream world of make-believe . . ." This is as accurate a picture as anyone could paint of what life is like for Don Quixote; for the old man truly *does* believe everything that is written in his romantic books of long ago. There he is now, sitting under that apple tree, musing about the latest adventures of some starry-eyed young hero in a novel. Let's listen to him—

DON QUIXOTE: "And they lived happily ever after." (*Sighs*) I'm glad it all came right in the end, but I'm sorry that the end has come so fast. With so much evil in the world, it's nice to read about some goodness once in a while. But why should there be evil in the world? Surely it could be stamped out. Of course. Why should this thought, which so suddenly jolts into my mind like a fistful of lightning, never have come to me before? At last, my mission in life is made clear. I must take up arms! I must mount my gallant steed! I must right the wrongs of the world, and thus do honor to my lady love! But . . . I have no arms, no steed. I have no lady love. How can that be? I know I am a true knight-errant, for I feel like one. Therefore I must be one. As for armor, I'll make myself a shield out of pasteboard and paint. My niece's old horse shall be my steed; I shall call her Rosinante, which signifies Finest Horse of All. And as for a lady love—there was a country girl in Toboso, once, who smiled at me as I passed her picking cabbages in a field. *She* will be my lady. I shall call her—I shall call her—Dulcinea del Toboso, and in her name I shall fight the gallant wars of knight-errantry. That's it. I shall have arms, a steed, *and* a lady love! Behold the knight-errant, Don Quixote!

MUSIC: *Happy theme.*

NARRATOR: While Don Quixote dreams his innocent dreams of glory, however, his niece, with whom he makes his home, is having an urgent conference with the local curate about her uncle.

NIECE: Satan take his books, and all his learning too, for they have robbed my dear uncle of his senses! Oh, what am I to do?

CURATE: Have you tried reasoning with Don Quixote?

NIECE: Reasoning! My uncle will listen to no reason. Unless what you have to say is filled with giants and sorcerers and captive princesses, he'll have none of your reasoning. Oh, I could cry with fury! His books, aye, all of them, deserve to be burned to ashes and cinders!

CURATE: They deserve to be burned, did you say? Why, there you have the very idea. Let us build a huge bonfire, and consign all your uncle's books to the flames. That, I warrant, will be the end of his foolish notions.

NIECE: Why, what a wonderful idea! And with what joy will I throw those volumes one after the other into the roaring furnace. But come, good curate. There's work to be done. We must haul down the bookshelves, set the wood afire in the grate. Please give me a hand. There's little time to lose.

CURATE: What a service this book-burning will be to Don Quixote. You, his niece, will prove his guardian angel in disguise.

NIECE: Come, good curate. Come to the library. We'll bring back my uncle's sanity yet.

MUSIC: *Active theme.*

NARRATOR: Imagine Don Quixote's dismay when, upon arriving home an hour later, he sees his precious volumes of magic, sorcery, fiction and fact, his treasures of knighthood's legends, heaped in a blazing pile on the hearth, the smoke of learning curling up the chimney.

DON QUIXOTE (*In anguish*): Niece! Niece! What devilry have we here?

NIECE (*Fading on*): Oh, Uncle, a most dreadful thing has happened! A most frightful thing!

DON QUIXOTE: Most frightful, most dreadful indeed! What are all my books doing in the fireplace? Why are they enveloped by flame?

NIECE (*Stammering*): Now don't be angry, Uncle, for it's not of my doing. A—a sorceress came into the house.

DON QUIXOTE: A sorceress, you say?

NIECE: Well, I *think* she was a sorceress. She wore a black cloak and had a long white beard.

DON QUIXOTE: Yes, yes; that would be a sorceress, all right.

NIECE: Well, she—she took all your books and threw them onto the hearth. Then she said a—a magic word.

DON QUIXOTE (*Excitedly*): What magic word did she say?

NIECE: I—I don't remember. I didn't hear her too clearly. At any rate, the books went up in flames.

DON QUIXOTE (*Wailing*): Oh, what is to be done? What is to be done?

NIECE: It seems to me that you are to give up all your reading nonsense. That's what's to be done.

DON QUIXOTE: Never! Whoever did this dastardly deed must be punished. I must be avenged! Niece, bring me my sword!

NIECE (*Incredulously*): Uncle, what are you saying?

DON QUIXOTE: I have sworn an oath to right all the wrongs of this world, in the name of my beloved, Dulcinea del Toboso. The time has come, I see, for me to journey forth into the world on my mission. Farewell, my niece. I must go! (*Fading*) Make way for Don Quixote of La Mancha!

NIECE (*In despair*): God help us all! My uncle is madder than ever.

MUSIC: *Lighthearted theme.*

NARRATOR: And so Don Quixote, his hopes high, his determination strong, puts on his pasteboard helmet, takes up his rusty lance and clambers onto the back of his rickety, underfed, overworked horse, whom he has named Rosinante. As he trots his way across the village square in ridiculous splendor, he is hailed by the village loafer and ne'er-do-well, one Sancho Panza.

PANZA: Ho, there! Don Quixote! Where are you off to on this fine day, in that ludicrous costume?

DON QUIXOTE: Infidel! Only your ignorance, Sancho Panza, prevents my lopping off your head for such an insult to the knight-errant who has pledged himself to the service of Dulcinea del Toboso! Ludicrous indeed!

PANZA: Knight-errant, eh? Night-*mare*-ant would be more like it, I'd say. Where are you going, Quixote?

DON QUIXOTE: I go to seek my fortune in the world. I go to avenge the wrongs done me by some unnamed but horrible sorceress. I go to enforce justice in the country, to replace evil with honor.

PANZA: Quite a job you've cut out for yourself. And you're going on this wild goose chase alone?

DON QUIXOTE: Although a true knight should have a squire, I cannot allow the lack of one to prevent me from fulfilling my mission.

PANZA: But who will protect you, old man?

DON QUIXOTE: I shall need no other protection than mine own good right arm, and the love of my lady, the fairest of the fair, Dulcinea del Toboso. But it does seem a shame that I have no squire to accompany me, for a true knight may never gather riches, and I am sure to encounter great wealth along my journey.

PANZA: Great wealth, eh?

DON QUIXOTE: There is no question about it, Sancho Panza. Now, if I had a squire—

PANZA: He would be allowed to keep the fortune?

DON QUIXOTE: Exactly. Also, if I were to find a man worthy and willing to serve as my squire, I would make him Governor of the Island.

PANZA: Governor of the Island? What island?

DON QUIXOTE: Of whichever island I conquered first. Or, if I happened to annex a kingdom or two, my squire would fare even better. (*Sighs*) But alas, Sancho, I have no squire. No one will benefit from my journeys.

PANZA: What's wrong with *me*, Don Quixote?

DON QUIXOTE: You?

PANZA: Aye, me! Sancho Panza! I could be of great help to you, certainly. And I wouldn't mind picking up a little gold along the way, if it happened to come across our path, of course. Why not accept me as your squire?

DON QUIXOTE: Do you have a gallant steed?

PANZA: I have a gallant donkey named Dapple.

DON QUIXOTE: Very well, then, Sancho Panza. You may be my squire.

PANZA: One thing more, though. When I become governor of this island, will my wife, Teresa, become governess?

DON QUIXOTE: Who doubts it? Teresa shall be governess, with a golden crown upon her head.

PANZA: And a fine place for her, too, on an island! Since she is to gain as much from my traveling with you as I am, I don't see that she would object to my accompanying you.

DON QUIXOTE: What could she have to object to in your accompanying the most noble knight of all, Don Quixote of La Mancha?

PANZA: Nothing, I suppose—but then, you don't know my wife, Teresa.

TERESA (*Screaming, far off mike*): Sancho! Sancho Panza!

PANZA (*Quickly*): That's my little ladybird calling me now. Let's hurry and be on our way.

DON QUIXOTE: Surely you aren't afraid of facing your wife, Panza.

PANZA (*Quickly*): No, no, no, of course not. It's just that I'd hate to see her tears at my farewell. (*Fading*) Come, then, Don Quixote, let's be on our way.

TERESA (*Screaming, far off mike*): Sancho, you lazy good-for-nothing! Sancho Panza!

MUSIC: *Gay theme.*

NARRATOR: And so, Don Quixote of La Mancha, and his faithful—if somewhat henpecked—squire, Sancho Panza, plod out of their little village, and make their way to the highway which will lead them to adventure, nobility and rich reward. Much to Sancho's amazement, his master seems to have no definite route in mind, but is content to go whichever way his poor old nag, Rosinante, may lead him. For several days they travel in this desultory fashion, finding neither rest nor adventure; and soon Sancho Panza begins to worry about the chance of running out of food.

PANZA: Good Don Quixote, enough of this foolishness. Where is the adventure you have been talking so much about? Where are the riches and kingdoms we were so sure to find? For days now, all I've seen is the back of your head and the rump of your horse. Enough!

DON QUIXOTE: Patience, worthy squire. There is evil enough in the world, and I am confident that soon we will come upon a wrong that must be righted.

PANZA: Oh, we'll come upon one all right—if we don't starve to death beforehand! Our supply of food is sorely depleted. There's barely enough for one more meal, and I am already getting hungry.

DON QUIXOTE: You will have food and drink enough when we get to your island. And riches, too.

PANZA: Have you seen any island since we left La Mancha? I haven't. I've seen goats and sheep and fields of wheat galore, but not a single island have we come across, although my eyes are near bulging out of their sockets in the search.

DON QUIXOTE: Peace! I see something right now—something more important to us than islands.

PANZA (*Excitedly*): What is it? Perhaps some bread and cheese that some travelers have forgotten in their haste? Or an inn where we can find food and lodging?

DON QUIXOTE: Look over there, Sancho Panza! I see giants!

PANZA (*Terrified*): Gi—gi—giants?

DON QUIXOTE: We have found our first adventure! Those are evil giants that must be conquered! See how they stretch out their arms to bar our way?

PANZA: But, sir! Those aren't giants. Those are windmills.

DON QUIXOTE: Hmph! How like your simple ways, Sancho, to mistake those giants for windmills. And *evil* giants they are, too. I understand that they can reach down with their long arms and pick up a man, though he be fifty miles away.

PANZA: Fifty miles! Then aren't we a little too close to them, sir?

DON QUIXOTE: I will go closer yet. If you're afraid of them, you can stay behind, and let me charge them alone.

PANZA: They're only windmills. (*Reverently*) Lord, take care of my poor friend's muddled brain.

DON QUIXOTE (*Calling out*): Stand your ground, wicked

giants! I, Don Quixote of La Mancha, valiant knight-errant, challenge you to mortal combat! (*Fading*) In the name of Dulcinea del Toboso!

PANZA: He's rushing straight for them! (*Calling out*) Sire, it's a *windmill!* (*Agitated*) Why, he's charging! He's caught his lance in one of the sails! It's pulling him off his horse!

DON QUIXOTE (*Off mike*): Aiiii-eeeee!

PANZA (*Breathlessly*): Oh, Don Quixote, speak to me! Speak to me! Don Quixote, are you all right?

DON QUIXOTE (*Moaning*): I can't tell you how painful that fall was, because it's against the rules of knighthood to complain.

PANZA: But at least you're alive, sir, and that's something.

DON QUIXOTE: Oh, those evil giants! Just as I was about to attack, they turned themselves into windmills. Cowards! Cowards! No doubt it was a trick of that same sorceress who destroyed my library.

PANZA: Don Quixote, your lance has been broken into splinters. What will you do for another?

DON QUIXOTE (*Grandly*): I'll do what the books say *all* knights did in similar circumstances. Sancho Panza, the next time we come to an oak tree, remind me to pull it up—by the roots.

MUSIC: *Rollicking theme.*

NARRATOR: After his first adventure of tilting with windmills, Don Quixote finds that the business of being a knight is even easier than he would have believed. Everywhere he looks, whichever way he turns, he seems to come face to face with another daring adventure.

PANZA: Let us move over to the side of the road, Don Quixote, to make room for this coach that approaches.

DON QUIXOTE: Make room for it, did you say? Foolish Sancho Panza, we must stop the coach and challenge the driver.

PANZA: Challenge the driver! Have you lost your wits, sir? It is only a lady, being accompanied on her travels by a Benedictine friar. Why must we challenge them?

DON QUIXOTE (*Laughing*): A lady! Accompanied by a friar! Oh, my poor friend, any simpleton can see at once that it is a captive damsel in distress, being carried off by some brigand.

PANZA: You're mad to say it. Why don't you admit that she is just a traveler?

DON QUIXOTE: I am not deceived, and as a knight-errant, it is my duty to stop the villainous kidnaper and set the lady free. Stop, you blackguard, and proceed no farther!

FRIAR (*Fading on*): Peace be with you, good sir. Why do you call me blackguard, and why do you block our way?

DON QUIXOTE: Cursed villain, set this princess free!

FRIAR (*Perplexed*): What princess?

LADY (*Slightly off mike*): Why have we stopped, good friar?

DON QUIXOTE: Fair princess, I, Don Quixote of La Mancha, have delivered your highness from the clutches of this evil abductor.

LADY: Good friar, what is he talking about?

FRIAR: Madam, I believe his wits are strayed. Good sir, will you let us pass?

DON QUIXOTE: Never, as long as she is your prisoner.

PANZA: Good master, listen to reason!

DON QUIXOTE: Quiet, Sancho! Sir, I challenge you in the name of the fairest of the fair, Dulcinea del Toboso!

LADY: Oh, please, sir, don't fight over me!

DON QUIXOTE: Rest easy, my lady. I ask no reward for saving you, but that you let everyone know that it was I, Don Quixote, that was your rescuer.

FRIAR: For the last time, sir, will you let us pass?

DON QUIXOTE: Never! Draw your sword, sir! Have on!

SOUND: *Clash of swords.*

LADY (*Screaming*): Heavens! Have mercy! The man is mad!

DON QUIXOTE (*Triumphantly*): There, madam, the deed is done. See how the villain's head is beneath my foot. I have conquered him.

LADY (*Angrily*): You fool, he is no villain, but my good friend, and a monk of the Benedictine order—as good a man as ever lived. Let him up this instant, I tell you!

DON QUIXOTE: Only if he will promise to go to Toboso at once, and let the gallant Dulcinea see for herself how I have laid him low for her sake.

LADY: He'll promise you anything—*anything*—only let him up so that we may continue our journey.

DON QUIXOTE (*Graciously*): Your wish, good princess, is my command. Arise, you blackguard, and escort this lady in safety to her destination! And do not forget for an instant that it was only her efforts on your behalf that allowed you to escape with your life.

LADY: Come along, Friar. The man is mad.

FRIAR (*Fading*): Mad he is indeed.

DON QUIXOTE: Well, Sancho Panza, my squire. Now you know how it is done, this business of vanquishing the villains of the world. Did I not complete the task with dispatch?

PANZA (*Shuddering*): You did indeed . . . God forgive you for it!

DON QUIXOTE (*Confidently*): I see now that there is no great difficulty in being a knight-errant. I shall have no trouble at all in fulfilling my mission. World of adventure, make way for Don Quixote!

MUSIC: *Gay theme.*

NARRATOR: With such a knack for turning innocent events into the most glorious of medieval sallies, Don Quixote finds ample opportunity for displaying his gallantry on every hand.

PANZA (*Coughing*): Plague take these clouds of dust! A man can hardly see in which direction his donkey is carrying him.

DON QUIXOTE: Plague take the dust, indeed! What do you think causes it, my worthy squire?

PANZA: It's plainly the herds of sheep that are crossing the road, sir.

DON QUIXOTE: Nonsense! There's only one thing could make the dust rise so high and hard.

PANZA: I'm almost afraid to ask what you think it is!

DON QUIXOTE: It is an enemy army. And where there is an army, there are oppressed peasants. We must ride to their rescue!

PANZA: No, no, sir, that is no army; it is—

DON QUIXOTE (*Interrupting*): I say it is an army! Listen to their barbaric cries of "Baaa! Baaa!" Stay here and wait for me, Sancho. I shall fight them singlehanded! (*Fading*) Take heart, my peasant friends, for Don Quixote rides to your rescue! Chaaaaarge!

PANZA (*Weakly*): First it was windmills. Then a poor Benedictine monk. Now Don Quixote is off to fight his gallant fight with a flock of sheep. Oh, Lord in Heaven, what next?

MUSIC: *Lighthearted theme.*

DON QUIXOTE: Look, Sancho! A magician's castle! We must storm it! (*Fading*) In the name of Dulcinea!

PANZA (*Calling out*): That's no castle, Don Quixote. It's an inn.

MUSIC: *Quivering chord.*

DON QUIXOTE: Wait here, Sancho Panza! I see another task for my knightly arm. Up ahead—a procession of enchanted goblins. (*Fading*) In the name of Dulcinea!

PANZA (*Aghast*): The man is mad. That's a funeral—with torchbearers.

MUSIC: *Another chord, higher than the first.*

DON QUIXOTE: Look, my friend. There lying in the road, is just what I am in need of. A helmet. Help me put it on.

PANZA: But, sir, that's no helmet. It's a basin.

DON QUIXOTE: I say it is a helmet, Panza. Help me put it on.

MUSIC: *Another, higher chord.*

DON QUIXOTE: Look, Sancho. There, up ahead. What is that line of men?

PANZA (*Frightened*): Oh, sir, don't bother with them. They're prisoners of the law. See how they are chained, one to another? Don't have anything to do with them, sir. You'll only cause trouble.

DON QUIXOTE: It is my job as a knight, Sancho, to help those in distress, to free those who are enslaved. Perhaps I can help these miserable fellows.

PANZA (*Fading*): Well, sir, this is one adventure I'll have nothing to do with.

DON QUIXOTE: Very well, then, I shall proceed alone. You, sir. How do you happen to be chained up like that?

1ST PRISONER (*Plaintively*): Oh, sir, I am a prisoner because of love. I fell in love with someone else's wallet.

DON QUIXOTE: And you, fellow. Why are you chained hand and foot?

2ND PRISONER: Good sir, I am chained for singing. Under torture, I sang a song of treason.

DON QUIXOTE: And what's *your* reason for being a prisoner, my good man?

3RD PRISONER: I am here for being confused. I was confused between what was mine and what was somebody else's.

GUARD (*Fading on*): You there, old man!

DON QUIXOTE: And who might you be, who walks about free while the others here wear chains?

GUARD: I'm the prison guard, that's who I am. And these men are my prisoners.

DON QUIXOTE: Then you are the one who has the key to open the locks that chain these men together?

GUARD: Indeed I am, and I'd like to see someone try and take it from me!

DON QUIXOTE: Well, sir, I am the man who will try. I am Don Quixote of La Mancha, as gallant a knight as ever rode a steed. These men have committed crimes of which I, too, am guilty: loving, singing, and being confused. They must be released at once! Hand over the key!

GUARD: You must be mad, old stranger. These men are criminals. They go to the galleys.

DON QUIXOTE: If you will not give me the key, I must challenge you for it.

1ST PRISONER: Don't be a fool, Don Quixote.

2ND PRISONER: The guard is younger than you—and stronger.

3RD PRISONER: You'll never get the key away from him.

GUARD: The prisoners are right, old man.

DON QUIXOTE: It is my mission to right the evil in the world, so I must try. Put up your fists, guard!

GUARD: All right, old man, if you insist. But you'll be sorry.

SOUND: *Grunts, as they fight.*

1ST PRISONER: The guard will murder him!

2ND PRISONER: I can't bear to watch it!

3RD PRISONER: But look! Don Quixote is winning!

2ND PRISONER: He must be a sorcerer!

3RD PRISONER: The guard is down on the ground!

1ST PRISONER: Don Quixote has knocked him unconscious!

DON QUIXOTE (*Panting*): Once again I have proved that justice triumphs over evil! Here is the key, my friends, and with it, your freedom. Never forget, though, that your rescuer was Don Quixote of La Mancha, and he saved you in the name of the fairest of the fair, Dulcinea del Toboso!

MUSIC: *Happy theme.*

NARRATOR: After these and many other adventures, Don Quixote and Sancho Panza find that the road they are following leads them back to La Mancha. When they reach their own village again, they resolve to visit with their friends and families for a few days before setting out again on further adventures. Everyone flocks to the home of poor old Don Quixote's niece to listen to the old knight tell of his adventures, but when he speaks, they laugh at him in disbelief, and Don Quixote decides that he will find happiness again only by taking to the road. He sends word to Sancho Panza, who is visiting with his wife, Teresa, to tell him that they will be leaving La Mancha on the morrow.

PANZA: Well, wife, I shall be off on the road again with Don Quixote tomorrow.

TERESA (*Angrily*): Tomorrow! Did you say you're leaving me again to go on your fool's errand tomorrow, husband Sancho?

PANZA (*Meekly*): Gently, Teresa, my wife. It is what Don Quixote wishes.

TERESA: I am tired of what Don Quixote wishes. Don't my wishes count for anything? For months you've been away from La Mancha, and now, after only two days at home, you're off again.

PANZA: Surely you wouldn't want the old man to go alone, would you?

TERESA: Why not? Just because he's a fool, you don't have to be one as well.

PANZA: But I—I enjoy our journeys together.

TERESA: You *enjoy* them? You mean to tell me that you like all this dancing and prancing across the countryside, on foolish errands that never put a scrap of silver into your pocket?

PANZA: It's something that's hard to explain. I—I believe in Don Quixote.

TERESA: That madman?

PANZA: He's not mad! He may sound mad, but there's sense in everything he says. Besides, I promised him I would go with him, and I never go back on my word.

TERESA: He's a lunatic! Where is the island he promised you?

PANZA: You'll see, Teresa. Some day I shall have my island.

And when Don Quixote gets it for me, I'll send for you straight off.

TERESA: Don Quixote! Don Quixote! I wish I had never heard the name of Don Quixote.

PANZA: No, no, my wife. You should be thankful that you know him and that I have the honor of being a squire to him.

TERESA: And why, may I ask?

PANZA: Because Don Quixote is a man in love—in love with justice, and truth, and with noble causes.

MUSIC: *Sentimental theme, in and under.*

NARRATOR: Early the next morning, the Knight of the Woeful Figure, Don Quixote of La Mancha, and his trusty squire, Sancho Panza, once more mount their steeds and leave their sleepy village in search of further adventure. How they fight great battles, with grand victories, find their wonderful island, and come face to face with the real Dulcinea del Toboso—these stories are told in Miguel de Cervantes' immortal classic, *Don Quixote.*

DON QUIXOTE (*Valiantly*): In the name of Dulcinea del Toboso, make way for Don Quixote of La Mancha.

MUSIC: *Triumphant theme, full to finish.*

THE END

Martin Chuzzlewit

Martin Chuzzlewit

by Charles Dickens

Characters

SARAH GAMP	MARY GRAHAM
THREE GOSSIPS	YOUNG MARTIN CHUZZLEWIT
ANTHONY PECKSNIFF	TOM PINCH
OLD MARTIN CHUZZLEWIT	

MUSIC: *Light theme. Up, under, and out.*

SARAH GAMP (*A gossipy old Cockney woman*): First of all, you needn't wonder how I happen to know the whole and truthful story of Mr. Martin Chuzzlewit. No, indeed. Many's the person that wonders where I find out all about the people I know the life histories of, and so I'll tell you straight out that Sarah Gamp is no fool. I've done a deal of night-nursing and day-nursing in my time, I can tell you, and anyone who keeps his ears half as open as I do can find out anything he wants to know. As a matter of fact, the whole story of Martin Chuzzlewit has been written down in a book by some no-account busy-body named Charles Dickens, but anyone of you who has read that book has *not* been told the entire truth of the matter. For the things that Mr. Dickens has to say about some of my weaknesses, and the "asperjions"

43

he makes on the character of myself, Sarah Gamp, are "libelious" and "slanderious" and wholly contrary to the fact. Being a lady, I'm not the one to talk about myself; but neither am I the one to ignore the insults about me that Mr. Dickens has seen fit to indulge himself in. So I'll just tell the story of Martin Chuzzlewit, and carefully *omit* all mention of myself, as is suitable to a modest lady of my *sterling* character and *noble* reputation.

Now then! The story all began when a mysterious old gentleman, accompanied by an equally mysterious and very beautiful young lady, arrived at the Blue Dragon Inn, not too far from London.

1st Gossip: I wonder who that old codger with the young woman is.

2nd Gossip: Never saw them before in my life. Hey there, Joe! Who's the strange couple that just took up lodgings here?

3rd Gossip (*Fading on*): Well, no one knows for sure, but I've heard that it's—promise you won't breathe a word?

1st Gossip: My lips are sealed.

2nd Gossip: You can depend on me.

3rd Gossip: Well, they say it's Martin Chuzzlewit.

1st Gossip: No!

2nd Gossip: Martin Chuzzlewit?

3rd Gossip: The same. Mr. Martin Chuzzlewit, the richest man in London, and cousin to our own townsman, Anthony Pecksniff.

1st Gossip: Hey, Mrs. Tupkins! Martin Chuzzlewit's in town!

2nd Gossip: Did you hear the news, Jacob? Martin Chuzzlewit's in town!

3RD GOSSIP: Hello, everybody. Martin Chuzzlewit's in town!

MUSIC: *Gay theme. Up and out.*

SARAH GAMP: How the word ever got around so fast is far beyond me to know, for there isn't a soul in our whole town that gossips or tattletales. But get around it did, for Martin Chuzzlewit was the richest man anybody in our village had ever heard of, and he was a first cousin by direct blood to Anthony Pecksniff, the town architect, and as stingy a man as you'd ever hope to meet. In no time at all, old Anthony Pecksniff was down to the Blue Dragon, his coattails flying in the breeze, the gleam of gold coins in his eye, the hope of his cousin's last will and testament in his heart, and the handle of Martin Chuzzlewit's door in his hand.

PECKSNIFF (*Falsely jovial*): Forgive my entering without knocking, sir. You are Martin Chuzzlewit?

CHUZZLEWIT (*Harshly, in voice of old man*): I am Martin Chuzzlewit, and Martin Chuzzlewit wishes you had been hanged before you had come here to disturb him.

PECKSNIFF: My good cousin—

CHUZZLEWIT (*Breaking in, angrily*): There! In his very first words, Mary, he asserts his relationship to me. I knew he would! They all do it! Ugh!

MARY (*Sweetly, soothingly*): There, there, Mr. Chuzzlewit. Do not upset yourself.

PECKSNIFF: This young woman gives you good advice, Chuzzlewit.

CHUZZLEWIT: And do you know why she does so, Pecksniff? Because she has nothing to gain for it. She is not related or bound to me in any way, and she knows that when I die she will not inherit a cent of my money, and so she —sweet, young thing that she is—has proved herself faithful and honest with me in every way. But you—

PECKSNIFF: Sir, you have no cause to judge me until you know me better.

CHUZZLEWIT (*Wearily*): I know *all* men—only too well. I am a rich man, Pecksniff, who has no pleasure in the possession of money. That is why you come here to me, hoping to butter me up, to win my confidence, and to be included in my will when I die. Confess it.

PECKSNIFF (*Self-righteously*): You do me wrong, sir. I came to you out of feelings of affection, of family concern.

CHUZZLEWIT: Bah! Your feelings of affection! Strange that they should bring you hither only when I am wealthy and old, isn't it?

PECKSNIFF: Sir, I care little for what you may think of me. But I feel it my duty—yea, my sacred obligation, to speak to you about your grandson.

MARY (*Too quickly*): Young Mr. Martin?

PECKSNIFF: Just so. Young Mr. Martin Chuzzlewit. Out of family concern for him, I have allowed him to become my apprentice in the architecture business, though he had not a farthing to his name. Now that I know you can afford to give him money, I shall urge you to do so, sir.

CHUZZLEWIT: So that you can take it away from him? Not likely! My grandson is no better than you are.

MARY: Oh, no, Mr. Chuzzlewit. No! You know young Mr. Martin is a fine man.

CHUZZLEWIT: Do you take his side against me, Mary? How many times have I told you that he only pretends to love you because he thinks it will bring him closer to my heart—and my pocketbook?

MARY: You do him wrong, sir. Young Mr. Martin's love for me is pure.

CHUZZLEWIT: And as for you, Pecksniff, be off with you. If you thought that by taking my grandson into your business you would inherit some of my money, you were mistaken. Not a pound will go to that young rapscallion. Not a shilling! Not a penny!

PECKSNIFF (*Slyly*): I see. In that case, good day to you, cousin. (*Fades off.*)

CHUZZLEWIT: Good day and good riddance.

SOUND: *Door closing.*

CHUZZLEWIT: Oh, Mary, Mary! You see what men are? Gold is all they know. Only you, Mary, only you, who have everything to gain from my living and nothing to lose by my dying, only you are my friend. And that is the only kind of friend I have . . . or will have.

MARY: There, there, good Mr. Chuzzlewit. Rest now. Pecksniff is gone and will trouble you no more. Rest, sir.

MUSIC: *Unhappy theme. Up and out.*

SARAH GAMP: Old Martin Chuzzlewit had laid his finger on the pulse of Anthony Pecksniff, let me tell you. And once that old, scheming, miserly blackguard heard that there was no money to be gained from his apprentice, young Martin Chuzzlewit, a fine, young man, he dashed to his home as fast as he could, where he delivered himself of a righteous—oh, *very* righteous—sermon against the young man.

PECKSNIFF: Mr. Martin Chuzzlewit, sir.

MARTIN: Yes, Mr. Pecksniff?

PECKSNIFF: How you have deceived me, Martin! How you have put upon my innocent nature!

MARTIN (*Aghast*): I! Deceived you, sir?

PECKSNIFF: Oh, don't play that holy-innocent act with me, young man, for I have found you out! I have just been with your grandfather and his companion at the Blue Dragon Inn . . .

MARTIN (*Hopefully*): Mary is at the Blue Dragon?

PECKSNIFF: If that is the young woman's name, she is there, sir, and they have filled me with the truth of the kind of man you are. And to think that I trusted you, that I opened my home and office to you! Oh, it makes my blood run cold to think of such villainy as yours!

MARTIN: Mr. Pecksniff, you astound me!

PECKSNIFF: Villains are *always* astounded when they are found out, sir. Leave my house at once, young Martin Chuzzlewit. I never wish to see you again. Do you hear me? I wish you to leave my house at once.

MUSIC: *Turbulent theme, in and under.*

SARAH GAMP: Poor young Martin! No wonder he was astounded. How could he know that his only fault was to be in the bad graces of his wealthy grandfather, and that the only reason Pecksniff had taken him in was the hope of Martin's inheriting a fortune from the old man, and then marrying one of the Pecksniff daughters. Having been forced out of the Pecksniff house—and that, I may say, was the best thing that could have happened to him—Martin went immediately to the Blue Dragon Inn, to see his grandfather and his beloved Mary Graham.

CHUZZLEWIT: Ah, so you've come to see me again, have you, Martin?

MARTIN: Yes, Grandfather, and I sincerely hope that this visit will end more happily than did our last encounter.

CHUZZLEWIT: The only way for us to part civilly is if you say "Goodbye" at once and leave me, Martin. That will prevent our having words, which we are sure to do if you stay.

MARY: Oh, Mr. Chuzzlewit, be not so hard upon him.

CHUZZLEWIT: Mary, you don't know this young blackguard as I do.

MARTIN: Blackguard! You speak to me in the same tone that Pecksniff did.

CHUZZLEWIT: You had words with Pecksniff then, did you?

MARTIN: I did not, Grandfather, for he would not give me time to speak. Instead he called me blackguard and villain, and I know not what other names, and told me to leave his house, never to return.

CHUZZLEWIT: Did he then? Anthony Pecksniff has more sense than I gave him credit for.

MARTIN: Then it *was* you that turned him against me! He said as much, but I refused to believe you could speak so ill of me.

MARY: You see, Mr. Chuzzlewit? Martin believes only good of you.

MARTIN: Thank you, Mary, my love.

CHUZZLEWIT: A fine man, you think him, eh, Mary? Now that he has lost one benefactor, he comes snooping around me to see if I will be his next.

MARTIN: No, indeed, sir!

CHUZZLEWIT: Do you deny it, sir?

MARY: Dear Mr. Chuzzlewit, let your grandson speak on his own behalf.

CHUZZLEWIT: Well, I'd rather hear him do it than hear you speak for him.

MARTIN: If Mary speaks for me, it is because she loves me; and that is just, for I love her.

CHUZZLEWIT: Not you! All you love is my money! You profess love to my ward only because you know she is the one friend I have in the world, and you hope to gain something by it.

MARTIN: I do hope to gain something by it, Grandfather, and that is her hand in marriage.

MARY: Martin, my love, do you mean it?

MARTIN: I am yours, Mary, if you will have me. Say "Yes," Mary, do.

MARY: I cannot marry you, Martin, without your grandfather's permission.

CHUZZLEWIT: And that you will never have.

MARY (*Tearfully*): Only hear me, Mr. Chuzzlewit! Good Mr. Chuzzlewit!

CHUZZLEWIT: Spare me your tears, Mary. They will do no good. Sir . . .

MARTIN: Yes, Grandfather?

CHUZZLEWIT: You have been attempting to corrupt the trusting innocence of this loyal girl, and by so corrupting the one person in the world who has no designs on my fortune, you hope to become a rich man. Do not presume to state otherwise; I know what *all* men are: faithless, grasping, hard and unfeeling, interested only in gold. I only wish I could dispose of you altogether.

MARTIN: I only wish to dispose of myself, Grandfather, to dispose of myself in marriage.

CHUZZLEWIT: Very well, then. Let it be to anyone you like, but not to my Mary Graham.

MARY: Mr. Chuzzlewit!

CHUZZLEWIT: Make any other marriage, Martin, and I shall provide handsomely for you in my will. Marry Mary, and I shall cut you out without a shilling. There you have it: either renounce her, or be renounced by me.

MARY (*Tearfully*): Oh, Martin, Martin!

MARTIN: Never fear, my love. You mean more to me than all the gold in London. Keep your fortune, Grandfather! I shall marry Mary some day, and provide her with a fortune of my own.

CHUZZLEWIT (*Laughing*): A fortune of your own! And where do you propose to find such a thing? Is it going to drop from the sky?

MARTIN: I shall sail to America. It is a new country, and there I shall stay till I have earned enough to come back to England and claim my bride. They need young architects in America!

MARY: America! Oh, Martin, it is so far away. So far!

MARTIN: It will only be for a while, my love. And then I shall be home, and we shall be happy. Farewell, my love!

MARY (*Crying gently*): Godspeed to you, dearest heart. Goodbye, Martin Chuzzlewit!

SOUND: *Door closes.*

MUSIC: *Romantic theme, in, under, and out.*

SARAH GAMP: Poor Mary Graham! Her heart nearly broke with the leaving of her beloved, old Mr. Chuzzlewit's handsome grandson. But no matter how much she pleaded with her old guardian, he wouldn't reconsider the case. Not he! He meant well enough, but he was bound and determined that all men were after his money, and he would trust nobody. Young Mary sighed over her faraway love, and took to thinking of him whenever she could spare a moment. One day, when her little heart was nigh to breaking in pieces, she entered an old church to pray. The church was empty, but it was filled with beautiful music from the organ, and when she went to see who was playing it, she saw a kindly looking but poorly dressed old servant.

MUSIC: *A triumphant hymn, played on an organ. Up full and out.*

MARY: How beautifully you play! I do hope you don't mind my listening to your music.

TOM PINCH (*Humbly*): No, indeed, miss, though I fear my music isn't good enough for the likes of you.

MARY: Too good, rather. It filled my heart and made my troubles seem bearable again. Thank you for that, sir.

TOM PINCH: Sir! Did you call me "sir"?

MARY (*Surprised*): Why, yes, sir.

TOM PINCH: Sir! Hardly anyone calls me that. Everyone just calls me by my right name: Tom Pinch. Last person to call me "sir" was a fine young man who lived at our house. But he's gone away, and so I'm only old Tom Pinch again. Nobody calls me "sir" since Master Chuzzlewit went away.

MARY: Chuzzlewit! Do you mean young Mr. Martin Chuzzlewit, by any chance?

TOM PINCH: Lord bless me if he isn't the very one! Finest gentleman I ever knew. He lived with us for awhile—with my master, I mean, for I'm only old Mr. Pecksniff's servant. And Mr. Chuzzlewit treated me like his equal. Better even! He was a fine man. Oh, how I miss him since he went off to America. That's where he is now, you see, there being some young woman he wanted to marry, but her guardian being set against it.

MARY: I am that young woman, Mr. Pinch.

TOM PINCH: You! Well, Lord bless me. You're surely pretty enough for him—begging your pardon, miss.

MARY: Oh, Mr. Pinch, to think that we should both long for the same friend! How fortunate my finding you!

TOM PINCH: I'm glad of it, too, miss—for at Pecksniff's I daren't mention his name, their being down on him and all. It does my heart good to be able to speak of him aloud.

MARY: And mine, too.

TOM PINCH: I've written him once, but I didn't receive any answer, which is just as well, I suppose, since I don't know how to read.

MARY: My letters have all gone unanswered as well. But if you can't read, how did you manage to write to him?

TOM PINCH: It wasn't a letter that I wrote. I just put a five-pound note in an envelope, and I had a friend of mine put on the address. I know how a traveler—especially a young man—can be in need of funds from time to time, and I was only too happy to be of help to such a fine gentleman as young Mr. Martin.

MARY: You have a kind heart, Mr. Pinch. It has done me good to talk with you. I must go now, but I hope to see you again. Already I am anxious for the chance to hear your organ music again and to talk with you about my beloved Martin.

TOM PINCH: Lord bless you, miss. And you a lady! I'm that grateful. And any time you need an errand run, or a message sent, I hope you'll call upon Tom Pinch.

MARY: I will indeed, Tom. I will indeed.

MUSIC: *Happy theme. Up full and out.*

SARAH GAMP: Little did Mary Graham know at that precise moment how great a help Tom Pinch would be to her some day. There's *some* that know a working person has his feelings, same as others, though *one* person I know, Mr. Charles Dickens, doesn't seem to know it, as I've already told you. But on with my story. Though Anthony Pecksniff had been disappointed in his first interview with old Chuzzlewit, he wasn't one to give up easily. Once he had the smell of gold in his nostrils, it was the devil's own work to take him off the trail of it. So, having gotten rid of young Martin, back goes Pecksniff to the Blue Dragon, as humble as you please, and pays another call on old Martin Chuzzlewit.

CHUZZLEWIT: Back again, are you, Pecksniff? What is it this time?

PECKSNIFF (*Eagerly*): Oh, cousin, cousin, how can you be so cold to me? Haven't I already proved to you how deep my loyalty to your interests goes?

CHUZZLEWIT: What's that? Loyalty to my interests?

PECKSNIFF: I don't mind telling you, sir, that it was only because you told me of your dislike for your grandson that I dismissed him from my office. Knowing that the person of young Mr. Chuzzlewit was unpleasant to *you,* it immediately became unpleasant to *me!*

CHUZZLEWIT: You mean, don't you, that you got rid of him once you discovered he could be of no financial aid?

PECKSNIFF (*Unctuously*): No, indeed, sir. For to tell the truth, just between us two, the boy is a very talented architect, and I could have turned a pretty penny by selling his work in London. But did the thought of money prompt me to keep him? No, indeed! "Pecksniff," said I to myself, "this boy may be valuable to you, but because he is odious to his grandfather, your family loyalty *demands* that you have nothing more to do with him!" And so I showed him the door. Now, what further proof could you have of my loyalty to your interests, dear cousin Chuzzlewit?

CHUZZLEWIT (*Taken in*): Well, bless you, cousin Pecksniff. I beg your forgiveness for having misjudged you at our last meeting—for misjudge you I did.

PECKSNIFF (*Flatteringly*): There is nothing to forgive. Truth to tell, I *respect* you for misjudging me!

CHUZZLEWIT: You respect me for it?

PECKSNIFF: It proves you're a cautious man. It proves you're no fool. And that's precisely why I've come back. I have just got wind of a little business venture that is guaranteed to make both our fortunes. I've already invested every cent of my money in it, and knowing what a *fine, shrewd, cautious* man you are, I was sure you'd like to act on my advice.

CHUZZLEWIT: Guaranteed, you say? And all your own money is invested in it, eh?

PECKSNIFF: Every cent. I expect to be a millionaire before the year is out.

CHUZZLEWIT: It sounds like a capital business, cousin. Again I apologize for misjudging you. I see now you are a man to be trusted—indeed you are the only man of worth I have ever met.

PECKSNIFF: It is kind of you to say so, cousin. Now as to the business venture . . .

CHUZZLEWIT: Bring up all the particulars on it, Pecksniff, and I'll look into it.

PECKSNIFF: Oh, cousin, why tire yourself with all these details? Why not just give *me* a draft on your bank, and I'll take care of the details. Surely you aren't afraid to trust me?

CHUZZLEWIT: Indeed I am not! Very good, I'll give you five thousand pounds.

PECKSNIFF (*Greedily*): Five thousand! Excellent, cousin! And rest easy in your mind. Leave everything to me!

MUSIC: *Evil theme. In, under and out.*

SARAH GAMP: There you have it! Old Anthony Pecksniff, as scheming a villain as ever crawled the face of this beautiful earth, had contrived to swindle old Martin Chuzzlewit out of five thousand pounds. The old man, oh, *he* was as innocent as a babe in arms. He trusted old Pecksniff to the letter, and soon the two were as thick as if they'd been raised in the same cradle. Months went by, and every time old Martin would ask Pecksniff for information about the business, the answer would always be:

PECKSNIFF (*Craftily*): Oh, business is very good. *Very* good! Of course, at the moment we're turning all our profits back into the firm. But some day soon, Chuzzlewit, you'll be a millionaire!

SARAH GAMP: Or else the talk would go something like this:

PECKSNIFF: You want to talk to the solicitor of the business, cousin? Well, as it happens, just at the moment he's off to the Continent on a buying trip. And the book-keeper—oh, yes, he's gone with him. But don't worry about your money, cousin. Leave everything to me!

SARAH GAMP: And all the time, old Chuzzlewit kept being taken in by his false friend, the smooth-tongued Pecksniff. One day, Tom Pinch approached the Blue Dragon Inn and delivered a note for Mary. Imagine her surprise when, on tearing it open, she discovered it was from young Martin!

MARY: What's this? Martin's handwriting! He must be in London. Oh, happy, happy hour! His fortune must be made, and we are to be reunited. I can barely keep my hands still enough to read his words. "My dear Mary: It will surprise you, no doubt, to find that I am in London."

MARTIN (*On filter mike, if possible*): "It surprises me, too, I admit. You see, Mary, America was far less than I had hoped it would be, and I return to London not wealthy, as I had hoped, but impoverished. However, take heart, my love. Tom Pinch has told me something that may yet be our salvation. Till I come to you, trust in me, and please believe that all will be well. I shall come to the Blue Dragon Inn at eight o'clock tonight. I understand that my grandfather is to meet my old enemy, Anthony Pecksniff, at that time, and I intend to confront them together. Say nothing of all this to anyone, and have faith. Till eight o'clock, then, all my love, Martin."

MARY: "All my love, Martin." To think that I shall see him tonight! But why may I not say anything about his return? What is this mystery? I am so happy . . . and so afraid.

MUSIC: *Mysterious theme. In, under, and out.*

SARAH GAMP: That night, promptly at eight o'clock, Anthony Pecksniff arrived at old Martin Chuzzlewit's rooms.

PECKSNIFF: Good evening, cousin. I hope I find you in good health.

CHUZZLEWIT: You do indeed, Pecksniff. Mary, aren't you going to greet our guest?

PECKSNIFF: I kiss your hand, dear Miss Graham.

MARY (*Coldly*): Good evening, Mr. Pecksniff.

CHUZZLEWIT (*Reproachfully*): Mary! Is that the way to greet my dearest friend? For be assured that Anthony Pecksniff *is* my dearest friend.

MARY: So you have often told me, Mr. Chuzzlewit. But I have yet to see the proof of it.

PECKSNIFF (*With exaggerated hurt*): Oh, Miss Graham! Miss Graham!

SOUND: *Knock at door.*

CHUZZLEWIT: Who can that be?

MARY (*Happily, involuntarily*): Martin!

CHUZZLEWIT: What's that, Mary?

MARY (*Fading*): I'll see who is at the door, Mr. Chuzzlewit.

SOUND: *Door opening.*

CHUZZLEWIT: Martin!

MARTIN (*Fading on, briskly*): Good evening, Grandfather. Oh, Mary, Mary, my love!

MARY: Martin!

PECKSNIFF: Tom Pinch! What is the meaning of your coming here? I did not send for you! Go home at once!

TOM PINCH (*Fading on*): Excuse me, Mr. Pecksniff, but I am no longer your servant. I hand in my resignation as of this moment.

PECKSNIFF: Have you gone mad, Tom Pinch?

TOM PINCH: No, sir. Though you'll soon have cause to wish that I *had* gone mad before you spilled your secrets in front of me.

CHUZZLEWIT: What is the meaning of this, Martin?

MARTIN: I'll answer your questions in a moment, Grandfather. First, I must ask some of my own. Mr. Pecksniff!

PECKSNIFF (*Coldly*): Sir?

MARTIN: What is the nature of this business you have convinced my grandfather to sink his fortune into?

PECKSNIFF: Er . . . I . . . I . . . that is all none of your affair, sir.

MARTIN: See how he squirms and blushes, Grandfather? Tom Pinch, tell my grandfather what you have already told me.

PECKSNIFF: Tom Pinch, I order you to hold your tongue!

MARTIN: What are you afraid of, Pecksniff? Go on, Tom.

TOM PINCH: Well, sir, Mr. Chuzzlewit . . . there is no business!

CHUZZLEWIT: What's that?

MARTIN: Do not run for the door, Pecksniff. Two of my friends are waiting to intercept you. Two very strong friends, I might add. Sit down.

MARY: What does he mean, there is no business?

MARTIN: Just that. Pecksniff has taken Grandfather's money and deposited it in his own bank account. He is a fraud!

CHUZZLEWIT: Pecksniff! Is this true?

MARTIN: Ask yourself, Grandfather. Have you ever had any profits?

CHUZZLEWIT (*Slowly*): No.

MARTIN: Have you ever visited the place of this so-called business?

CHUZZLEWIT: No.

MARTIN: Have you ever met the board of directors? Do you know the bookkeeper? Have you spoken with the solicitor? Have you seen the product?

MARY: I can answer for him: no, no, no, and no!

CHUZZLEWIT: Oh, Pecksniff, Pecksniff, who would have believed it?

TOM PINCH: One thing more, Mr. Martin. I suggest you look at that roll of architectural plans Mr. Pecksniff is carrying.

PECKSNIFF: Keep your hands off these plans! They're the drawings for the new elementary school which the city has just commissioned me to design.

TOM PINCH: Only they aren't *your* designs, Mr. Pecksniff, they're Martin's.

SOUND: *Rustling of papers.*

MARTIN: Why, so they are, Tom. These are the very drawings I designed when I was apprenticed to Mr. Pecksniff. I'll wager the city paid him a pretty price for them, too. All he's done is add a few windows.

PECKSNIFF: Adding those windows makes all the difference!

MARTIN: It certainly does. It turns a beautiful building into a hideous one. Well, Grandfather, are you satisfied?

CHUZZLEWIT: Oh, what a fool I've been. What a fool I've been. Can you forgive me, Martin?

MARTIN: With a full heart, sir . . . on two conditions.

PECKSNIFF: Humph! Conditions! I *told* you he was after your fortune!

CHUZZLEWIT: That doesn't bother me. I'd rather have a fortune-hunter for a grandson than a thief for a cousin. What are your conditions, Martin?

MARTIN: First, that you employ Tom Pinch as your personal servant, and pay him well.

TOM PINCH (*Happily*): Oh, sir!

MARTIN: Come now, Tom, don't be modest. You've done my grandfather a great service this day, and you're in need of a job . . . unless you'd rather go back to Pecksniff.

TOM PINCH: Oh, no, sir! Never that!

PECKSNIFF: To think that I should hear my own servant mock me!

MARTIN: Be quiet, Pecksniff. You deserve far worse. My second condition, Grandfather, is that you allow Mary Graham to become my bride.

MARY: Oh, Martin!

CHUZZLEWIT: Gladly, Martin, my boy. I judged you hastily, and I fear I judged you cruelly. Let me know that I have your forgiveness.

MARTIN: You have indeed, Grandfather. But what's to be done about Pecksniff?

CHUZZLEWIT: He shall be forced to repay every penny he stole from me, and, for using your building design, to give you double the amount he has been paid.

PECKSNIFF: I shall be ruined!

MARY: Does he not deserve something stronger?

CHUZZLEWIT: We can do nothing worse to him, my dear, than he has done to himself, for he has robbed himself of dignity, integrity and self-respect. And what is worse than that?

MARY: Oh, Martin, I can hardly believe it. My love, oh my love!

MARTIN: Then you will have me, Mary?

MARY: With all my heart, my love. It will be the fulfillment of my dearest dreams. Mrs. Martin Chuzzlewit!

CHUZZLEWIT: God bless her and her husband, and keep them happy always.

CHUZZLEWIT, MARTIN *and* TOM PINCH: Mrs. Martin Chuzzlewit!

MUSIC: *Romantic, triumphant theme. Up full.*

THE END

Five Weeks in a Balloon

Five Weeks in a Balloon

by Jules Verne

Characters

FIRST MAN	DR. SAMUEL FERGUSSON
SECOND MAN	JOE, *his servant*
THIRD MAN	A MISSIONARY
DICK KENNEDY	NARRATOR

1ST MAN: Cross Africa by balloon? The man is mad!

2ND MAN: It's the most ridiculous thing I've ever heard.

3RD MAN: But they say the Royal Geographical Society has given him twenty-five hundred pounds for the adventure.

2ND MAN: The thing is impossible. It simply can't be done.

1ST MAN: The poor devil will never come back alive.

2ND MAN: I can tell you one thing: if any man on earth *can* do it, that man is Dr. Samuel Fergusson.

MUSIC: *Active theme, in and under. Out.*

NARRATOR: In 1862, the idea of traveling across the then uncharted continent of Africa was truly incredible. And to contemplate a trip by balloon seemed so fantastic that many men, indeed, thought Jules Verne, who first proposed the idea, was mad. In the books Verne wrote about the impossible, the absurd, the unimaginable—

Twenty Thousand Leagues Under the Sea; A Trip to the Moon; Around the World in Eighty Days—characters were always doing the impossible, contemplating the inconceivable. And yet, less than one hundred years after Jules Verne wrote his imaginative, fantastic novels, the things that he dreamed and wrote about have become realities. It is hard for us to imagine the reaction to the daring fantasy of one of Verne's most famous books: *Five Weeks in a Balloon.*

MUSIC: *Active theme, in and under. Out.*

NARRATOR: The events in this book took place in January, 1862. After many years of solitary work in his laboratory, the noted scientist Dr. Samuel Fergusson had perfected the invention which was the climax of his life's work. He constructed a giant balloon which could be navigated and controlled with an accuracy hitherto unimagined. With the Royal Geographical Society of London providing the financial backing, Fergusson determined to spend five weeks in his balloon, traveling across Africa, and from his aerial observation post, drawing maps which he believed would, for the first time, give an accurate picture of that continent. As our story begins, Fergusson is discussing his journey with the two men he proposes to take with him: the greatest sportsman of his time, Dick Kennedy; and Joe, the doctor's own servant, a man of unquestioned devotion and superior strength.

KENNEDY: You have quite made up your mind, then, Samuel, to go off on this fool's errand?

FERGUSSON: It is *not* a fool's errand, Dick, and I *am* quite decided upon it. Won't you change your mind and say you will come along? Your service on this journey is of the utmost importance to me.

KENNEDY (*Tentatively*): I don't know, Samuel. . . .

JOE (*Earnestly*): But you *must* come, Mr. Kennedy, if Dr. Fergusson wishes it.

FERGUSSON (*Kindly*): Dear Joe, not everyone follows me with such devotion as you do. Mr. Kennedy has a right not to wish to risk his life on what he calls a fool's errand, you know.

KENNEDY: Dash it all, Samuel, it's not that I mind the danger. I have risked my life many times with nary a thought. It's just that I don't want to be a party to what is certain to turn out a failure.

FERGUSSON (*Heatedly*): I tell you, Dick, my adventure cannot fail. The mechanism of the balloon is foolproof. I have thought the whole thing out so carefully.

JOE: If Dr. Fergusson says we will succeed, Mr. Kennedy, you may be sure we will succeed.

KENNEDY: You're quite sure you want me on this trip, Samuel?

FERGUSSON: So sure that I would not risk going without you. You and Joe are the only two men in all of England that I would care to have along; but without your services I cannot manage.

JOE (*Eagerly*): Oh, say you will come, Mr. Kennedy. See how much the doctor—how much we both—need you.

KENNEDY (*Capitulating*): Oh, very well. I wish I could believe in your project, Samuel, but I can't. I do promise, however, that I will do all I can to make the trip a success.

FERGUSSON (*Happily*): I knew you'd come around, Kennedy. You shan't regret it. And I promise you that you shall come to love that airship, to believe in her, as much as I do.

JOE (*Excitedly*): Wait till you see the balloon, Mr. Kennedy. Just wait till you see the *Victoria*.

KENNEDY (*Laughing*): I said I'd go, Joe. You needn't coax me any more. Gentlemen, I give you a toast: to the *Victoria,* and to the success of our five weeks in the balloon.

FERGUSSON: Excelsior!

MUSIC: *Active theme, in and under. Out.*

NARRATOR: The air was clear, and a moderate breeze was blowing on the day the *Victoria* was launched in Zanzibar. Packed in the traveling car were provisions, guns, munitions, water, and ballast—but not an ounce more than the weight the doctor felt was essential. The sailing was smooth and fine, and by the first night they had made good distance. When the stars came out, the three men looked about them, and they all felt closer to Heaven than they ever had before.

KENNEDY: It is the most beautiful sight I have ever seen.

JOE: Look at the stars! Thousands and thousands of them, and all of them twinkling.

FERGUSSON: It fairly takes the breath away, it is so beautiful.

KENNEDY: To think I might have missed this trip, just out of pig-headed stubbornness. Oh, Samuel—Joe—if I was not convinced before, I am now. Three cheers for the *Victoria!* We have embarked upon the adventure of a lifetime!

MUSIC: *Stirring theme, in and under. Out.*

NARRATOR: But all was not to be so peaceful and untroubled for the three travelers. Late that night, as they passed over one of the jungles inhabited by barbarous savages, they heard great cries and screams below them. Letting some gas out of the balloon, they lowered their craft sufficiently to have a look.

FERGUSSON: Give me the binoculars, Joe.

JOE: What do you see, doctor?

FERGUSSON: It's a tribe of savages. I can't quite make out what they are doing. Performing some sort of ceremonial rite, I think.

KENNEDY: Are they armed?

FERGUSSON: Some of them are—but they haven't spotted us. Let's hope that they are so engrossed in their activities that they don't. I don't know what they'd do if they captured three white men.

JOE: Shall we sail higher, doctor, to get out of their reach?

FERGUSSON: No. We'd only be more conspicuous against the sky. We must trust to luck. You two get some rest. I will keep watch. Let us hope we are not spotted.

NARRATOR: For several hours Dr. Fergusson stayed his post, never quite sure what was going on in the village of the savages—but never reassured until at last the noise died down, and the group of savages disappeared into the jungle. He was just about to lie down in the car of the balloon himself, when far away he heard a sound—a sound both strange and familiar.

MISSIONARY (*Far off mike*): Help! Help, help!

FERGUSSON (*Tensely, in close*): Joe! Wake up! Listen!

KENNEDY: What is it?

MISSIONARY (*Far off mike*): Help!

KENNEDY: By Jove! It's an Englishman—and in trouble!

FERGUSSON: We must go to him at once. To your places, men!

MUSIC: *Exciting theme, in and under. Out.*

NARRATOR: Guided only by the faint voice in the darkness calling for help, the men maneuvered their ship until they were over a clearing. There below them, a horrible sight met their eyes—a dying missionary lying on the ground, the victim of the cruel savages.

MISSIONARY (*Somewhat closer*): Help!

JOE: We must rescue him, doctor. Perhaps you can save him.

FERGUSSON: Poor fellow, I'm afraid he's past all human healing. But we cannot leave him here. If he should recover, we can bring him back to civilization, but if he should die, at least we can see to it that he has a decent burial.

MUSIC: *Somber theme, up and out.*

NARRATOR: Carefully manipulating the complicated controls of the balloon, the doctor caused the ship to lower slowly until it reached the ground. After dropping anchor, the three men clambered out and gently lifted the dying man into the car of the balloon. The doctor did all he could for the fellow, but it was too late. Though he slept for a while, he quietly slipped away during the night while the balloon was floating gently across the face of the sky. The next day the three agreed to land, and give the poor missionary a proper grave.

KENNEDY (*Soberly*): I little thought when we packed this shovel aboard that it would first be used to dig a grave.

FERGUSSON: We must be grateful that it is within our

power to give this man a decent resting place beneath the earth.

JOE: It is too bad that he could not have died in his own country, but must be laid to rest in a foreign land, far from his relatives and friends.

FERGUSSON: Perhaps that is best. They say a missionary loves the land to which he is sent to do his work better even than his homeland. Have you noticed, though, what a curious trick fate has played?

KENNEDY: What do you mean, Samuel?

FERGUSSON: The poor fellow we have just buried was a missionary. He took a vow of lifelong poverty. And yet we have buried him in earth that is full of gold.

JOE: Gold!

KENNEDY: Explain yourself!

FERGUSSON: Look at these rocks that you have dug up. Each of them is worth a fortune.

JOE: Then we are rich. Rich!

FERGUSSON: I'm afraid not, Joe. We cannot afford to take them. They would add too much weight to our load.

KENNEDY: But you don't mean you propose to leave a fortune behind us! There must be a way of taking it— or at least some of it.

FERGUSSON: I don't see how.

JOE: I know! We have aboard the ship two hundred pounds of ballast. Why not take the gold in its place? If worse comes to worst, we can use the gold for ballast and throw it overboard. And if we don't ever need to discard it, it will be our fortune!

FERGUSSON: Very well, Joe. We may take just so much of this ore as will replace the ballast. But you must understand that if it is ever necessary, we must be ready to cast it overboard without a second thought.

NARRATOR: The three explorers replaced the ballast in the balloon with the gold ore and set off again on their journey. That night, Dr. Fergusson entered in his diary the record of the day's adventures. And on his charts, he was able to mark the cherished notation:

FERGUSSON (*Speaking as he writes*): All—is—well. Progress —excellent—as—predicted.

NARRATOR: As the days went by, progress continued—but there were many adventures, dangerous and unexpected. On one occasion, when they had landed to refill their water tanks at a jungle stream, they were attacked by lions, and it was only Dick Kennedy's sharpshooting that saved the men's lives. On another occasion, the wind died down altogether, and the ship could make no progress at all. At first, the three adventurers were not alarmed; but when a sandstorm blew up, the men dropped anchor and sought refuge in the desert. There they were forced to stay for three days, long after their supply of water had been exhausted. The heat was unbearable, and they almost succumbed to thirst. But at last the rains came, and once again they were on their journey. From the desert they were crossing in the direction of Lake Tchad, when suddenly the doctor spoke in a serious tone:

FERGUSSON: There's trouble ahead, men. Look over there!

KENNEDY (*Amazed*): But it's just a flock of birds.

JOE: Why should a flock of birds mean trouble, doctor?

FERGUSSON: Those birds are condors. If they decide to attack, they can destroy the balloon instantly with their claws. Take your rifles, men, and keep them trained on the lead bird. If they try to get within striking distance, shoot for all you're worth!

NARRATOR: Dr. Fergusson's worst fears were soon realized. The birds did indeed wheel in toward the balloon, but in such a way that the balloon itself hid them from view, making it impossible to shoot. There was a moment of silence, and then there came the terrifying sound of silk being ripped apart as the birds attacked the balloon with their razor-sharp claws.

FERGUSSON: We are lost! Throw out the ballast!

KENNEDY: Willingly, Samuel. I can feel us sinking already!

FERGUSSON: I'm sorry to order the end of your fortune, Joe, but there is no other choice.

JOE: To save us, sir, I'd throw it overboard if it were the Bank of England itself!

SOUND: *Rocks being thrown out.*

KENNEDY: Have we saved enough weight, do you think?

FERGUSSON: I cannot tell yet. Keep throwing the ore over the side.

JOE: There, that is the last of it.

FERGUSSON: Still not enough. Throw over the water barrels, Joe.

SOUND: *Scuffling and barrels being thrown out.*

KENNEDY: We're still sinking!

FERGUSSON: Then give me a hand with the provisions. Throw out everything!

SOUND: *Scuffling of men lifting and throwing out provisions.*

JOE: There they go! Has that done the trick? There's nothing left to discard.

KENNEDY: And we are still sinking!

FERGUSSON (*Seriously*): Gentlemen, if there is nothing else to throw overboard, we are lost.

JOE: Wait, doctor, wait. (*Fading*) There is one thing more!

FERGUSSON (*In a panic*): Joe! Don't!

NARRATOR: But there was no time to stop him. In an instant the young servant, Joe, had thrown *himself* over the side, and was plummeting from view into the waters of Lake Tchad below. But his sacrifice achieved its purpose: the balloon at last began to rise.

KENNEDY: Oh, Samuel, he's lost. Lost!

FERGUSSON: Yes, Dick. He has given his own life—to save us.

MUSIC: *Dramatic theme, up and out.*

NARRATOR: For two whole days the survivors traveled on without speaking. All their thoughts were on the young man who had so nobly died that the journey might be completed successfully. Though they said nothing, Fergusson and Kennedy both were thinking of only one thing. At last Kennedy broke the silence.

KENNEDY: Perhaps Joe is not lost after all, Samuel. No man in the world is stronger or more daring than he. If any man can survive in this cruel corner of the globe, that man is Joe.

FERGUSSON: Heaven grant you may be right, Dick! At any rate, when this trip to which we have pledged ourselves is over, we will come back to Africa, and search for him. We'll find out what happened to him, or die in the attempt.

KENNEDY: He risked his life for us. We can do no less for him.

MUSIC: *Serious theme, up and out.*

NARRATOR: On . . . on . . . on sailed the balloon. Each night Fergusson made his accustomed entry in his log. But now his heart was not in it.

FERGUSSON (*Sadly, aloud as he writes*): Progress—excellent —as—predicted. All—is—well.

NARRATOR: Day after day, night after night, the strange little ship, the *Victoria,* traversed her southward course across the sky. There were greater dangers, more terrifying experiences, more trying times with every passing day. But Dr. Fergusson and Dick Kennedy had staked their professional reputations on the trip, and they refused to give up. Through a combination of luck and skill, no matter how great the danger, they always managed to survive. As they were flying over the southern desert lands, Kennedy, who was standing watch, gave a shout.

KENNEDY: We may be in for more trouble, Samuel. Look —ahead, there.

FERGUSSON: It looks like a moving army.

KENNEDY: It's a band of Arabs—in pursuit of someone. Some of the riders are armed. I think we'd better reach for higher altitude.

FERGUSSON: Impossible. The balloon is so weather-beaten, so damaged from all she's been through, I can't get her any higher without a stronger wind.

KENNEDY: That's bad. Their shots can reach us at this height.

FERGUSSON: Have they spotted us?

KENNEDY: I don't think so. They're too busy chasing that fellow out in front.

FERGUSSON: I wonder why they want him.

KENNEDY: The only reason I can think of is that he's probably stolen a horse. These Arabs can forgive anything but horse theft.

FERGUSSON (*Chuckling*): Poor devil. He must have needed that horse pretty badly to risk being followed by such a mob.

KENNEDY: Look how beautifully he sits in the saddle. He's a young man, I think, to judge by his riding. I can almost make out his features with the binoculars. (*Pause, then excitedly*) Samuel! Samuel!

FERGUSSON (*Excitedly*): What is it, Dick? What is it?

KENNEDY (*Incredulously*): The man on the horse! The man they're after! It's—it's Joe!

MUSIC: *Exciting theme, up full and out.*

NARRATOR: There was no time to lose. Turning the control valves as hard as he could, Fergusson lowered the balloon, carefully engineering it so that it would move in the same direction as the leading horseman, and thus stay somewhat close to him. Now the Arabs could not help but see the balloon, and some of them began firing.

SOUND: *Shots being fired intermittently in background.*

NARRATOR (*Continuing without a break*): By now Joe himself had become aware of the *Victoria* over his head. At the crucial moment, Kennedy lowered a rope ladder from the balloon. The Arabs, whose attention had been distracted by the airship, did not see Joe grab the rope. With almost superhuman agility, he pulled himself out of the saddle, and scrambled up the rope ladder to safety. As soon as he felt Joe's weight tugging from below, Fergusson applied all his might to the control valves. Instantly, like a giant feather blown high by the wind, the *Victoria* soared into the clouds. The three men turned to face each other. Not a word was spoken, but each was blinking back his tears. Joe was alive! Joe was safe! (*Pause*) Joe was home! And that night Dr. Fergusson recorded the triumph in his diary.

FERGUSSON (*As he writes*): All—is—well. Progress—excellent—as—predicted. (*Pause*)

MUSIC: *Stirring theme, up full and out.*

NARRATOR: On the travelers pressed, now moving southward, now westward, taking meteorological readings, noting climatic conditions, filling in the spaces on maps that had been blank for centuries. The major part of their journey was over.

KENNEDY: To think, Samuel, that I had no faith in this expedition when I first heard of it in London.

FERGUSSON: You were not alone, Dick. Except for Joe, everyone thought me a madman—or, what is worse, a fool.

JOE (*Happily*): Did I not tell you, Mr. Kennedy, that if Dr. Fergusson said we would succeed, we should succeed?

KENNEDY: The *Victoria* is certainly the most amazing craft.

FERGUSSON: Alas, she is not in as good shape now as when we started. The adventures she has undergone have left their mark. I am afraid the heat of the furnace has melted the gutta-percha, for I find it lets out a little gas regularly—not much, but enough to be felt. Each day the *Victoria* can attain only slightly less altitude than the day before.

KENNEDY: Can nothing be done to remedy the situation?

FERGUSSON: Very little, I fear. That is why, from now on, we cannot stop at all, but must travel all day each day, and all night too.

KENNEDY: Then that is why you have been taking on fewer and fewer provisions at each stop—to make the traveling easier.

FERGUSSON: Right. Timbuktu is still four hundred miles away—and before we are safely there, we must pass the terrible mountains that separate the Niger from the basin of the Senegal. If only we can get over those mountains, all will be well.

KENNEDY: You doubt that we will make it?

FERGUSSON: It is too early to tell. We can only wait and see.

NARRATOR: Four days later, the *Victoria* passed over the Senegal country. The mountains now lay straight ahead. But the balloon was sinking more noticeably each day, and at last a conference was held to determine the best course of action.

KENNEDY: Tell me, Samuel, do you think we can gain enough altitude to pass over the mountain range at its lowest point?

FERGUSSON: Not as the ship is now. We'll never make it in our present condition.

KENNEDY: Then let us put down the anchor and make repairs. Surely we could remedy the situation.

FERGUSSON: It's true that we could probably fix the balloon sufficiently to guarantee us safe passage over the mountains. But the country of the Senegal is a dangerous place. Many explorers before us have been killed by the savages.

JOE: I would not put down for even an hour in this country if I could help it. The stories one hears are terrible indeed!

FERGUSSON: There is only one thing for us to do. We must

throw overboard everything not absolutely essential.

JOE: There is little enough to throw out by now.

KENNEDY: We can throw out the tent. It is very heavy.

FERGUSSON: Help me with it, then.

SOUND: *Scuffling, dragging, and fast breathing as men throw tent overboard.*

JOE: There! That should make the natives happy. There is enough fabric in that tent to clothe an entire tribe for years.

KENNEDY: And look, Samuel, we're rising!

FERGUSSON: But not enough. See: the mountains are still five hundred feet above us. Throw the water out of the furnace.

SOUND: *Splashing of water.*

FERGUSSON: That's better. But more is needed. Throw over the empty casks. (*Pause*)

JOE: There they go!

FERGUSSON: Dash it all! It's still not enough. If we don't get higher, we shall be smashed to bits.

KENNEDY: There's still about fifty pounds of meat. I'll get rid of that.

SOUND: *Scuffling and dragging noises.*

FERGUSSON: Still not enough. Dick, we must throw your firearms overboard.

KENNEDY: But I can't let them go! We may need them yet!

FERGUSSON: If you hold on to them, we will need nothing —ever again!

JOE: Please, Mr. Kennedy, they will cost us our lives.

KENNEDY: But they have already saved our lives, Samuel, and we may need them for the same purpose again.

FERGUSSON: We will simply have to chance that. Dick, you

must throw them over. We have only moments now, and we are still ten feet short of the height we need to clear the mountaintop.

JOE (*Suddenly*): Wait, Mr. Kennedy, wait. It won't be necessary after all.

FERGUSSON (*Sternly*): Joe, don't dare to go over again. We cannot spare you.

JOE: I will be safe. You just wait and see. (*Fading*) Never fear, doctor.

NARRATOR: Just as it seemed certain that the *Victoria* would crash headlong into the mountainside, Joe gave a mighty spring out of the balloon. Without his weight to carry, the balloon soared upward, and by the smallest margin possible managed to clear the mountaintop.

JOE (*Off mike*): That's it! She is clear! Throw me a rope, and be quick about it!

NARRATOR: The valiant Joe had held on to the bottom of the balloon until the crucial moment, when he had allowed himself to drop, landing feet first on the very crest of the mountain. As soon as the balloon had cleared, he grabbed the rope, and by a strenuous effort succeeded in pulling himself back into the car again.

FERGUSSON: Oh, Joe, Joe, my brave fellow, we have no right to let you risk your life for us.

JOE: This time it was not for you, Dr. Fergusson. It was for Mr. Kennedy's rifle. He saved my life with it that time I was attacked by the lion. I have only returned a favor.

KENNEDY: Good for you, Joe. I couldn't have parted with my rifle, I don't think—not even to save us all.

FERGUSSON: Well, my friends, the worst is behind us. From here on it should be no problem navigating our course. My friends, we have proved the world wrong. We have traversed the whole of Africa. We have succeeded in our magnificent undertaking. We have survived our journey —five weeks in a balloon.

ALL (*In unison*): Excelsior!

MUSIC: *Triumphant theme, full to finish.*

THE END

The Masque of the Red Death

The Masque of the Red Death

by Edgar Allan Poe

Characters

RED DEATH
WOMAN
DOCTOR
MAIDSERVANT
GENTLEMAN
LADY
PRINCE PROSPERO
TWO COUNCILMEN
PRINCESS CONSTANZA
TOWN CRIER
CHAMBERLAIN
SOLDIER
PEASANTS, COURTIERS

RED DEATH: Can you hear me, oh, children of the Light? Hark to my words. Hear what I do say, for I am the Red Death. None escapes my bloody scythe, nor rich nor poor. My sign is blood, my seal is pain. Hear me, oh, children of the Light, for I am Red Death.

MUSIC: *Eerie theme, in and under. Out.*

WOMAN (*Pleading*): Oh, Doctor, thank Heaven you've arrived. Come in, come in. My husband . . . !

DOCTOR (*A bumbling sort*): Patience, good woman, patience. My coat . . . ?

WOMAN (*Impatiently*): Take the Doctor's coat, Gavin.

DOCTOR: Your boy? Fine-looking lad!

WOMAN: In here, Doctor. My husband. He's in such pain.

DOCTOR: Well, we'll try to fix him up as good as new. Is this the patient?

WOMAN: Yes.

SOUND: *Groans of a man.*

DOCTOR: Well, now, sirrah, what seems to be . . . (*In alarm.*) Father in Heaven!

WOMAN: Why do you start? What is it?

DOCTOR (*Fading, in alarm*): It's . . . Red Death!

SOUND: *Woman screams.*

MUSIC: *Ominous theme, in and under. Out.*

DOCTOR (*Calling aloud*): Red Death has struck again!

PEASANTS (*Ad lib*): Red Death! The plague! It strikes again! The cobbler is dead of the plague! Red Death has taken another! (*Etc.*)

SOUND: *The crowd noise subsides, but rumbles ominously beneath the following speech.*

RED DEATH: Yes, it is I, Red Death. I have killed again, this time a peasant. But I do not discriminate; do you remember my words: "Nor rich, nor poor. None escapes my bloody scythe."

MUSIC: *Ominous theme, in and under. Out.*

MAIDSERVANT (*Fading on*): My lord.

GENTLEMAN: How many times must I tell you not to break in upon me unsummoned?

MAIDSERVANT: But, my lord, the child is dead.

GENTLEMAN (*Stricken*): What?

MAIDSERVANT: The child . . .

LADY (*Fading on; weeping*): My lord, my husband. Our child . . .

GENTLEMAN: Dead?

LADY (*Weeping*): Aye, aye. Dead!

GENTLEMAN (*Tearfully*): Of . . . of what cause, woman?

MAIDSERVANT: Of the Red Death, my lord.

GENTLEMAN: The . . . Red . . . Death.

MUSIC: *Tragic theme, in and under.*

RED DEATH: Nor rich, nor poor, nor high, nor low, nor young, nor old. All, all must feel the chill of my breath, the pain of my kiss, the darkness of the tomb.

MUSIC: *Agitated theme, up and out.*

PROSPERO: And so, honorable gentlemen of my council, you have heard my decision. I must have fifty thousand gulden more for the Royal Budget.

FIRST COUNCILMAN: But Your Highness . . .

PROSPERO: But me no buts! I want the money; I will have the money.

FIRST COUNCILMAN: Where shall it come from?

PROSPERO: That isn't my concern, it's yours. Tax the people if you like.

SECOND COUNCILMAN: They are already taxed as much as they can bear.

PROSPERO: Then find it somewhere. Don't bother me with trifles. (*Angrily*) I have given my final word, gentlemen. That is all!

SECOND COUNCILMAN (*In submission*): Very well, Prince Prospero.

SOUND: *Door opening off mike.*

CONSTANZA: Husband Prospero, a word with you I beg.

PROSPERO: Gentlemen, may I present my wife, the Princess Constanza.

COUNCILMEN: Your Highness.

PROSPERO: What brings you to the Council room my dear?

CONSTANZA: I must speak to you about the Red Death. Something must be done!

PROSPERO (*Laughing*): Hear her, gentlemen of my Council. The Red Death! Is that what a prince must concern himself with? That is the problem of the peasants, my dear.

CONSTANZA: But hundreds of your people die each day, yet you do nothing.

PROSPERO: And what would you have me do?

CONSTANZA: Supply the people with doctors. Give them healthful food, and clean homes.

PROSPERO (*Greedily*): That would cost a fortune. Why should I bother myself about the Red Death. The walls around the palace keep him away from me. He doesn't dare show his face at court!

CONSTANZA: Alas, that is no longer true.

COUNCILMEN (*Ad lib*): What does she mean? Is there Red Death here at court? (*Etc.*)

PROSPERO: What do you mean, wife? Explain yourself.

CONSTANZA: Red Death has broken out in the servants' quarters here at court. Five of the lackeys, three of the grooms, one valet, and two of my best maids are dead of it.

PROSPERO: There are hundreds of servants!

CONSTANZA: If it were servants alone! But this morning, Red Death took the only child of your friend, the Earl of Hammond.

PROSPERO: What? The child? My god-daughter?

CONSTANZA: The same. Husband, husband, something must be done to help our people.

PROSPERO: Aye, Constanza, something must be done. Gentlemen of the Council, we must think of a plan. We *must* find a way.

MUSIC: *Urgent theme, up full and out.*

TOWN CRIER: Hear ye! Hear ye! As a protective measure against the Red Death, His Royal Highness Prince Prospero, along with five hundred of his lords and ladies, will go into a secluded retreat at Casa Venabla, on the highest mountain in our country. His Highness expects that there will he and his court escape the plague of the Red Death. (*His voice fades.*) Hear ye! Hear ye!

MUSIC: *Royal theme, in and under. Out.*

CONSTANZA (*Fading on angrily*): My husband, you promised that something would be done about the Red Death.

PROSPERO (*Pleasantly*): And something shall. I have decided to go into a retreat, with five hundred lords and ladies . . .

CONSTANZA (*Disgusted*): Yes, I have heard your plan. So you are going to run away, leaving your people to die.

PROSPERO: If they must die, that's their business.

CONSTANZA: It's your business. You are their ruler, yet all you think of is your own neck. Do you really expect to escape the Red Death at Casa Venabla?

PROSPERO: It is the highest mountain in the country, windswept and desolate.

CONSTANZA: He'll find you there. There's no use running from him. You must do what you can to stop him.

PROSPERO: I have made my decision, Constanza. We leave for the deserted castle tomorrow.

CONSTANZA: Then you leave without your wife. I will not go.

PROSPERO: What?

CONSTANZA: I will stay here.

PROSPERO: Stay here and die?

CONSTANZA: If die I must, then die I will, but I shall not desert our people. They need me as they have never needed me before. I will not let them down, Prospero.

PROSPERO: You are more a fool, Constanza, than I thought. All right! You have decided to stay. I will allow it. I shall not alter your decision. Do not attempt to alter mine.

MUSIC: *Determined theme, up and out.*

PROSPERO (*Bored*): What news of the Kingdom, Chamberlain?

CHAMBERLAIN: The plague rages still. Ah, Your Highness, how wise it was of you to escape with all of us to this lonely spot. Red Death will never find us here.

PROSPERO: You are right, my Chamberlain. Red Death will never find us here.

MUSIC: *Royal theme, up full and out.*

CHAMBERLAIN: Your Highness. Good news!

PROSPERO: I could use some good news, Chamberlain. Cooped up in this old castle with these foolish lords and ladies for months without end, I am bored and sick at heart. What is your news? I am more than eager for it.

CHAMBERLAIN: The plague has vanished from the kingdom.

PROSPERO (*Delighted*): Good news that is indeed!

CHAMBERLAIN: Your wife, Princess Constanza, has led the people in their fight against Red Death.

PROSPERO: So, she has done it, after all. We will be returning then, Chamberlain. Let it be known throughout this desolate castle. No, wait. Proclaim a Masqued Ball, at which all the lords and ladies must be present. Say there will be a contest for the most grotesque costume, by way of a celebration, a *divertissement*. But do not tell them the news. I wish to tell it to them myself.

CHAMBERLAIN (*Fading*): Yes, Prince Prospero.

MUSIC: *Regal theme up full, hold; then, into ball music, in and under.*

SOUND: *Ad lib of* COURTIERS *softly in background.*

CHAMBERLAIN (*Calling out*): Musicians, cease your playing!

MUSIC: *Out.*

CHAMBERLAIN: Lords and Ladies, I present our honored host, His Royal Highness, Prince Prospero.

SOUND: *Applause of the courtiers.*

PROSPERO: Good evening, welcome guests. You wonder, I am sure, why I have called upon all of you to attend this ball. I have some great and good news for all of you.

SOUND: *Ad lib of courtiers.*

PROSPERO: The Plague has been chased from our capital. The city is no longer ridden with Death. We shall all go home tomorrow.

SOUND: *A shout of rejoicing from the courtiers.*

PROSPERO: Our siege against the Red Death has succeeded. We are . . .

SOUND: *Clock striking twelve.*

PROSPERO: But, hark! The time is midnight. We must have the grand parade. Masqueraders all, form a line; make a procession before my throne. Here in this purse are twenty precious stones, and as many pieces of gold. This purse is his who wears the most grotesque costume. Players, begin!

MUSIC: *A slow march, in and under. Out.*

PROSPERO: Very nice! Interesting! How wonderful and weird! Well, how exotic! My, so strange! Ladies and gentlemen, a thousand pardons, pray. Each of your costumes is so unusual, so grotesque, I know not to whom I should give the prize:

SOUND: *A windowpane breaking.*

RED DEATH (*Off mike, in bold tones*): Prince Prospero, *I* claim the prize.

SOUND: *Several women scream.*

PROSPERO: How dare you!

RED DEATH (*Fading on very slowly*): Is not my costume the most grotesque, the most awful you have ever beheld? See how my vesture is dabbled in blood. And my brow and the features of my skull-like face, see how they are besprinkled with the scarlet horror?

PROSPERO (*Losing his nerve but attempting to conceal the fact*): Who dares to impersonate Red Death? Who dares insult us with this blasphemous mockery? Seize him, soldier, and unmask him—that we may know whom we have to hang at sunrise, from the battlements!

SOLDIER (*Afraid*): I dare not go near him, Sire!

PROSPERO: Chamberlain, then!

CHAMBERLAIN: I also fear, Your Highness.

RED DEATH: No one dares come near me. You are all afraid. Because you know who I am.

PROSPERO: Who . . . what are you?

RED DEATH (*Slowly*): I am Red Death.

PROSPERO: But . . . but my wife . . . the people . . . they have driven you from the city.

RED DEATH: From the city, yes. But I had to flee somewhere. And so I came hither. I am thirsty, Prince Prospero. I have come here to this bleak, forsaken place, to slake my thirst.

PROSPERO: What . . . what would you drink?

RED DEATH (*After a pause*): Blood.

SOUND: *Women screaming.*

MUSIC: *Triumphant, ghostly theme, in and under.*

RED DEATH: Can you hear me, oh, children of the Light? Hark to my words. Hear what I do say, for I am the Red Death. None escapes my bloody scythe, nor rich nor poor. My sign is blood, my seal is pain. Hear me, oh, children of the Light, for I am Red Death.

MUSIC: *Up full to finish.*

THE END

The Little Princess

The Little Princess

by Frances Hodgson Burnett

Characters

JESSIE, *twelve*	MR. BARROW
LAVINIA, *thirteen*	MR. CARMICHAEL
LOTTIE, *six*	MR. CARRISFORD
MISS MINCHIN	RAM DASS
SARA CREWE, *twelve*	NARRATOR

NARRATOR: Many years ago, in one of the fashionable streets of London, there stood an imposing building, on the door of which was nailed a shiny brass plate, engraved with the inscription, "Miss Minchin's Seminary for Young Ladies." Miss Minchin's—the school where little girls of wealthy families studied music, French, geography, history, embroidery, and the other subjects which a lady of breeding was expected to master. Our story is of one such little girl, Sara Crewe, whose father was one of the wealthiest men in India. As our tale begins, several of Miss Minchin's pupils have gathered in the living room to discuss the new arrival.

JESSIE (*Excitedly*): She's the new show pupil! Her father brought her all the way from India, and her dresses are silk, every one of them! She has a doll that's as big as Lottie, and her name is Sara Crewe.

LAVINIA (*A spiteful child*): Hmph! Sara Crewe, indeed! It's a plain enough name. The way you carry on about her, Jessie, you'd think she were a little princess.

JESSIE: I believe you're jealous, Lavinia Herbert—jealous of the new girl.

LOTTIE (*A little girl*): Jealous! Jealous! Lavinia's jealous!

LAVINIA: Do be quiet, Lottie. As though there were anything to be jealous *of!*

LOTTIE: Yes, you are, too, Lavinia. Isn't she, Jessie? You're jealous of the new pupil that Miss Minchin has, Lavinia. You're jealous of the rich little new girl, Sara Crewe.

MUSIC: *In and under.*

NARRATOR: That afternoon, Miss Minchin called all the young ladies of the seminary together, and when they were assembled, she introduced their new classmate.

MISS MINCHIN (*A stern old maid*): Young ladies, your attention please. I should like to introduce you to your new companion, Sara Crewe. I shall expect you all to be very agreeable to Miss Crewe. She has just come from a great distance; in fact, from India. Although Sara's papa is very rich, it has not spoiled our new pupil, and I am sure you will find her as charming, intelligent and gracious as I have. Because she is older, Sara will set an example for you younger girls, and I'm sure that Miss Crewe will be, to all of us, a most welcome addition to Miss Minchin's Seminary for Young Ladies.

MUSIC: *In and under.*

NARRATOR: Sara was, indeed, a welcome addition to the seminary, especially to the younger girls, who loved her and looked to her for understanding.

SOUND: LOTTIE, *crying off mike.*

SARA (*A sweet-voiced girl*): Oh, Lottie, what are you crying for?

LOTTIE (*Through her tears*): I haven't any mamma, Sara.

SARA (*Seriously*): Neither have I.

LOTTIE (*Amazed*): Haven't you? Where is she?

SARA: My mamma has gone to heaven, Lottie, but I am sure she comes out to see me sometimes, though I don't see her. So does yours. Perhaps they can both see us now. Perhaps they are both in this room.

LOTTIE: Is that really true, Sara?

SARA: Some people might think that it's rather like a fairy story, but I enjoy pretending. If I pretend really hard, then it doesn't seem as much like pretending as it does real!

LOTTIE: Why are you always making up stories and pretending things, Sara?

SARA: It makes things easier to bear when I'm unhappy. I miss my papa a great deal, and I know he misses me, so I pretend things to help me become the sort of little girl he wishes me to be.

LOTTIE: What sort of things?

SARA: I pretend that I'm a princess. Princesses must never be cross or unhappy, you know, but must keep their tempers always, no matter what.

LOTTIE: Does it help you, Sara? Are you a good girl?

SARA: I don't know. It just happened that I was born with a father who is handsome and nice and clever, and can give me everything I like. Perhaps I am not really a good child at all, but if you have everything you like and everyone is kind to you, how can you help but be good-tempered? I don't know how I shall ever find out. Perhaps I'm a *hideous* child, and no one will ever know, just because I never have any trials.

LOTTIE: Lavinia has no trials, and she is horrid enough.

SARA (*Reflectively*): Perhaps that is because Lavinia is *growing.*

LOTTIE: I think she's dreadful! But you could never be dreadful, Sara. You're the most wonderful girl in the whole world!

MUSIC: *In and under. Out.*

NARRATOR: Not all the girls, of course, were as quick to love and admire Sara as was little Lottie. Lavinia Herbert, an advanced thirteen, thought Sara was horrid, and Lavinia wasn't bashful about discussing her views on the subject.

LAVINIA (*Mimicking* MISS MINCHIN): Dear Sara must come into the drawing room and talk to Mrs. Musgrave about India. Dear Sara this and dear Sara that. And as for her papa, there is nothing so grand in being an officer in India.

JESSIE: He has killed tigers. He killed the one that's the rug in Sara's room. That's why she likes it so and talks to it as if it were a cat.

LAVINA: She's always doing something silly. My mamma says that her always pretending things is silly. She'll grow up eccentric.

JESSIE: I heard her father just invested in some *diamond* mines!

LAVINIA: As for the diamond mines, that's the whole reason Miss Minchin plays up to Sara, because she's so rich.

LOTTIE (*Fading on, crying*): I heard you, Lavinia. Stop talking about Sara that way.

LAVINIA: Stop crying this minute, Lottie, or Miss Minchin will hear. You stop this minute, you crybaby!

LOTTIE (*Crying harder*): I'm not a crybaby!

JESSIE (*Coaxing*): Lottie, darling, if you stop, I'll give you a penny.

LOTTIE (*Still crying*): Don't want your old penny! Here comes Sara! She loves me!

SARA (*Fading on*): Lottie, dear, why are you crying so, pet?

LOTTIE: She—Lavinia—she said I was a crybaby, Sara.

SARA: But if you cry, you will be one, Lottie, you know. Come and sit in the window seat, and I'll tell you a story.

LOTTIE (*Sniffling*): Will you tell me about the diamond mines?

LAVINIA: The diamond mines! That's all you talk about. Nasty spoiled thing, every time you talk about them, I'd like to slap you.

SARA (*Angrily*): Well, I'd like to slap *you!* But I shan't slap you. We are not little gutter children. We are both old enough to know better.

LAVINIA (*Sarcastically*): Ah, yes, your royal highness. We are princesses, I believe—at least one of us is. The school ought to be very fashionable, now Miss Minchin has a make-believe princess for a pupil.

SARA: It's true. Sometimes I do pretend I am a princess. I pretend I am a princess so that I can try to behave like one.

LAVINIA (*Fading*): Dear me! I hope, when you ascend the throne, you won't forget us!

MUSIC: *In and under. Out.*

MISS MINCHIN: Girls! On this, the occasion of Sara Crewe's birthday, I wish to make a little speech, before you go

into the other room for your refreshments. When her
dear papa, Captain Crewe, brought Sara from India and
left her in my care, he said to me in a jesting way, "I am
afraid she will be very rich, Miss Minchin." My reply
was, "Her education at my seminary, Captain Crewe,
shall be such as will adorn the largest fortune." Sara has
become my most accomplished pupil. Her French and
dancing are a credit to the school. Her manners, which
have caused you to call her Princess Sara, are perfect.
Her generosity is shown by her giving you this party. I
hope you appreciate her kindness. I wish you to express
your appreciation of it by saying aloud all together,
"Thank you, Sara."

GIRLS (*In singsong unison*): Thank you, Sara.

SARA: Thank you for coming to my party.

MISS MINCHIN: Very pretty indeed, Sara. That is what a
real princess does when the populace applauds her. And
now I will leave you to enjoy yourselves. Happy birthday, Sara Crewe.

MUSIC: *In and under. Out.*

NARRATOR: The girls all trooped into the living room, and
there, spread on a glistening white tablecloth, were de-
licious candies and cakes. In one corner of the room
stood a huge pile of presents. But while Sara and her
friends were having a good time, Miss Minchin was talking to a strange, official-looking gentleman in her office
—a gentleman who was to bring bad news for Sara.

MISS MINCHIN: Yes, sir? What can I do for you?

MR. BARROW: Miss Minchin? My name is Mr. Barrow. I'm
from Barrow & Skipworth. We are the solicitors for the
late Captain Crewe.

MISS MINCHIN: The "late" Captain Crewe! You don't mean to say that Captain Crewe is dead?

MR. BARROW: Unfortunately, that is true. Died of jungle fever and business troubles combined.

MISS MINCHIN: What were his business troubles?

MR. BARROW: Diamond mines, my friend, and ruin.

MISS MINCHIN: Ruin! You must be joking, Mr. Barrow! Captain Crewe was a man of fortune.

MR. BARROW: "Was" is the correct word. I regret to inform you that he is now dead, and the diamond mines are nonexistent. His fortune is used up to the last sixpence; his daughter, Sara, is an orphan and a ruined beggar.

MISS MINCHIN: Do you mean to tell me that he has left nothing? That Sara is left on my hands a little pauper instead of an heiress? What am I to do? What?

MR. BARROW: I don't know, ma'am. Barrow & Skipworth is not responsible.

MISS MINCHIN: Has she no relations who will take her and pay her bills? Then I shall turn her into the street. That horrid child will not become my responsibility!

MR. BARROW: I shouldn't do that if I were you, Miss Minchin. It wouldn't look well; would be an unpleasant story about the seminary. Better keep her and make use of her. She's a clever child, I believe. You can get a good deal out of her as she grows older.

MISS MINCHIN (*Excitedly*): To think of all those unpaid bills for silk dresses, a maid, and even for the birthday party she is giving right now in the next room. I've advanced the money for everything for that child, and now she cannot repay me. (*Harshly*) Mr. Barrow, I assure you I will get a great deal out of Sara Crewe before she grows much older. Yes, I will get a great deal from the little beggar, Sara Crewe, from now on!

MUSIC: *Harsh theme, in and under. Out.*

NARRATOR: Miss Minchin wasted no time in informing Sara of her poverty.

MISS MINCHIN: Everything will be different for you from now on, Sara. I suppose you understand that.

SARA (*Soberly*): Yes. My papa is dead. He left me no money. I am quite poor.

MISS MINCHIN: You are a beggar. Don't put on grand airs with me; the time for that sort of thing is past. You are not a princess any longer. You will wear your oldest and plainest clothes; your extravagant ones are no longer suited to your station. You will help in the classroom with the younger children, and work in the kitchen, running errands. You are like the scullery maid. You must work for your living from now on.

SARA: If I can work, it will not matter so much. What can I do?

MISS MINCHIN (*Snapping*): You can do anything you are told! If you don't please me, you will be sent away. Now go. Your room has been emptied, and your few dresses have been left in your *new* quarters in the attic. Stop! Don't you intend to thank me?

SARA: What for?

MISS MINCHIN: For my kindness to you in giving you a home.

SARA: You are *not* kind, Miss Minchin, and it is *not* a home.

MUSIC: *Unhappy theme, in and under. Out.*

NARRATOR: All of Sara's pretty things were put away. Her carriage was sold; her maid was dismissed. She moved out of the best suite in the house, and into a bleak, cold room in the attic, next to the scullery maid. She was no longer a student at the seminary; now she was a drudge, a servant. She missed the pretty things, the fine food, and the warm room, but most of all she missed seeing her friends, who were forbidden to speak to her now. So imagine Sara's surprise when one day she returned to her attic room and heard a voice . . .

LOTTIE (*Fading on*): Sara? Are you here?

SARA (*Surprised*): Lottie! What are you doing up here in the attic? You'll get into trouble if Miss Minchin finds out.

LOTTIE (*Stubbornly*): Don't care if I do. I miss you, Sara. It's been six whole months since you've been a servant instead of a little girl. Six months since I've been able to talk to you.

SARA: It's only half a year, but it does seem a long time.

LOTTIE: Do you sleep up here, in this dreadful attic, Sara? I should hate it; it's so cold and bare and poor-looking.

SARA: I don't mind it too much. I pretend it's the Bastille and that I'm a prisoner. Pretending always makes things easier. Remember that I once told you it was only pretending that made me act like a princess? You see, it's true. I'm not a princess any more.

LOTTIE: Oh, yes, you are, Sara. Whatever happens, you'll always be a princess, and nothing could make you different.

SOUND: *A scratching on wood.*

LOTTIE (*Frightened*): What's that?

SARA: It's only the rat family in the wall. They're quite friendly!

LOTTIE (*Aghast*): Are there really rats here?

SARA: Yes, and swallows, too. Come over to the window. See those birds on the roofs, flying around the chimneys? And a monkey lives in the house next door.

LOTTIE: A real monkey?

SARA: Yes. An old gentleman by the name of Mr. Carrisford lives in that house. He is an invalid and has an Indian servant by the name of Ram Dass who lives in the attic and keeps a pet monkey. Once the monkey ran away and came through the window right into this room.

LOTTIE: How wonderful!

SARA: Ram Dass and I are friends; we smile at each other from the windows. So you see, Lottie, it isn't too awful living in the attic.

LOTTIE: It's just like a story!

SARA: It *is* a story. *Everything's* a story. You are a story; I am a story. Even Miss Minchin is a story.

LOTTIE: Sara, that's one story I'd rather hear the end of!

MUSIC: *In and under.*

NARRATOR: Meanwhile, Mr. Carrisford, the old gentleman who lived next door with his Indian servant Ram Dass, was seated in his study, with his lawyer, Mr. Carmichael, who was trying to reassure Mr. Carrisford on a matter of great concern to him.

MR. CARMICHAEL: I tell you, Mr. Carrisford, we're doing everything in our power to locate young Sara Crewe. Everything!

MR. CARRISFORD (*In a weak but urgent tone*): We must find her, we must! To think that my friend Captain Crewe should have died before the diamond mines he owned became successful! Why, his little daughter, Sara, may be starving, when actually there are millions waiting for her. I could **never** forgive myself, Carmichael, if we don't locate Ralph Crewe's daughter and see that she gets the fortune that is hers.

MR. CARMICHAEL: I'll find her, Mr. Carrisford, rest assured. (*Fading*) I'm off to Moscow tomorrow. I heard that she may be there.

MR. CARRISFORD: I hope so, Carmichael. Goodbye, and good luck. (*Pause*) Ram Dass! Ram Dass, come here. I want you.

RAM DASS (*Fading on*): Yes, Sahib?

MR. CARRISFORD: I'm too upset to sleep, Ram Dass, my faithful servant. Talk to me, will you?

RAM DASS: Sahib worries about finding the little lost rich girl. Perhaps he would like to hear about another girl, a little poor girl?

MR. CARRISFORD: Eh? What poor girl?

RAM DASS: Sahib, you know that next door is a school for young ladies. In the attic, across from my own room, lives one such young lady, a very pretty child, but very poor. She seems to be a servant, but is the sweetest child I have ever seen. My monkey escaped to her room one day, and when she returned him, we became friends. She is a solemn child, though, and her room is very bare and plain. She has no fire; her bed is hard; her clothes are poor; and she seems never to have enough to eat.

MR. CARRISFORD: Do you suppose it possible that the other little girl—the child we have spent these last few months looking for, Sara Crewe—could she be reduced to such a state as the poor child next door?

RAM DASS: I am sure Miss Crewe is well taken care of, wherever she is, but perhaps it would make Sahib feel better to help the little girl next door.

MR. CARRISFORD: How could we do that, Ram Dass?

RAM DASS: I thought perhaps Sahib would buy some warm blankets, some clean dresses, some books and food for the poor child in the attic. At night, when she is asleep, I could carry them through her window. The roofs of our two houses touch, and she would be so pleased.

MR. CARRISFORD: Excellent idea, Ram Dass. We'll order the proper things at once. Perhaps if I try to make this little child happy, it will help me feel more sure about finding the child of my friend, the wealthy little Sara Crewe.

MUSIC: *Hopeful theme, in and under. Out.*

SARA (*Sleepily*): Mm . . . how warm I feel! Such a nice dream! I'm a princess, not a prisoner in the Bastille. Oh, I'm waking up! But I'm still warm! The warmth usually melts away when I wake up. Oh, I never had such a dream before! I'm dreaming it *stays* warm! I am dreaming it feels real! Blankets, and a real, crackling fire, and a dress at the foot of the bed, and a tray of soup and sandwiches! I'm bewitched! I only think I see it. If I can only *keep* thinking it, I don't care! How true it seems, and the blanket's warm and soft. The dress is real! And books! They're all real! And on the table—such good things to eat. Oh, it *must* be real. Why, what's this? A note by the table. It says "To the little girl in the attic. From a friend." I don't know who it can be, but somebody cares for me a little. It's true. Oh, Papa, Papa, I have a friend. I have a friend!

MUSIC: *Joyous theme, in and under. Out.*

NARRATOR: Now it didn't seem to hurt as much when Miss Minchin ordered Sara about.

MISS MINCHIN (*Sharply*): Go out to the bakeshop and buy bread for the cook, Sara. (*Pause*) Go up to the schoolroom and teach the younger girls their French, Sara. (*Pause*) Sara, do this. Sara, do that. Sara, go here. Sara, go there. You are a pauper, a servant. Do you hear? You are no longer a little princess, Sara Crewe.

MUSIC: *Unhappy theme, in and under.*

NARRATOR: All the time that Sara was running errands at the school, Mr. Carrisford, next door, was wondering how to go about finding her.

MUSIC: *Sad theme, in and under.*

MR. CARRISFORD: But how long must I wait, Carmichael? You have been searching for Sara Crewe for two years now, and still no sign of her!

MR. CARMICHAEL: We're doing the best we can, Mr. Carrisford. I've spent every waking hour in the search, but to no avail. The child we heard about in Moscow was three years older than Ralph Crewe's little girl, and the child in Paris was two and a half years younger. I've gone to every girls' school on the continent, but without success. I'm sure we'll find her, though. Don't lose patience, but give me time.

MR. CARRISFORD: Time, time. There's plenty of time and plenty of money. Use as much as you like, but find her, Carmichael, find her!

MUSIC: *Urgent theme, in and under.*

NARRATOR: Whenever she could, little Lottie would steal up to Sara's attic, to share with her the pleasures of having a secret friend.

LOTTIE (*Off mike*): Sara, may I come in?

SARA: Yes, Lottie, but close the door behind you. It would never do for Miss Minchin to find you here.

LOTTIE (*Excitedly*): Was there another gift from your secret friend today, Sara?

SARA: Yes, some books, and another fine meal. Lottie, these last two years have been magic.

LOTTIE: I wish I knew who it was that is making you so happy, and taking such good care of you.

SARA: I suppose we'll never know, since he wishes to remain anonymous. And we can't ask Miss Minchin about it, because—

LOTTIE: Listen! Something's at the window!

SOUND: *Scratching off mike.*

SARA: Yes. It sounds rather like a cat, trying to get in.

LOTTIE (*Excitedly*): Just suppose the monkey got away again. Oh, I hope it did!

SARA: Look, Lottie. It *is* the monkey! He has crept out of Ram Dass's attic, and he saw our light.

LOTTIE: Are you going to let him in, Sara?

SARA: Oh, yes! It's too cold for monkeys to be out. They're delicate. I'll coax him in.

SOUND: *Window being opened.*

SARA: Come along, monkey darling. I won't hurt you.

SOUND: *Monkey cheeping.*

SARA: Nice monkey. Oh, I do love little animals!

LOTTIE: He *is* rather ugly, isn't he?

SARA: Perhaps he's sorry he's so ugly.

LOTTIE: What shall you do with him?

SARA: I shall let him sleep with me tonight, and then take him back to the Indian gentleman tomorrow. I am sorry to take you back, monkey dear, but you must go. You ought to be fondest of your own family, and I'm not a real relation, you know.

SOUND: *Monkey cheeping gayly.*

MUSIC: *Gay theme, in and under.*

NARRATOR: In the home of the Indian gentleman next

door, the search for the little lost girl was becoming more and more intensive.

CARMICHAEL: Well, Mr. Carrisford, it seems to me there is only one thing to do. We have searched the schools in all of Europe. Let us give up on the continent and start to search London.

MR. CARRISFORD: There are schools enough in London. There is one next door!

MR. CARMICHAEL: Then we will begin there. We cannot begin nearer than next door.

MR. CARRISFORD: There is a child there that interests me —Ram Dass called her to my attention. A poor little creature, more a servant than a pupil. I've been trying to help her out these past two years.

RAM DASS (*Fading on*): Sahib, excuse me, but the child herself has come, the child that Sahib felt pity for. She brings back the monkey who again had run away to her attic under the roof. I have asked her to remain. Perhaps it will please Sahib to see and speak to her.

MR. CARMICHAEL: Who is she?

MR. CARRISFORD: Heaven knows! She is the child I spoke of, a little drudge at the school. Yes, Ram Dass, I should like to meet her. Go bring her in. (*Sound of door closing.*) While you have been away, Carmichael, the days were so dark and long. Ram Dass told me of this child's miseries, and together we invented a romantic plan to help her. Perhaps it was childish, but it gave me something to think of.

SOUND: *Door opens.*

RAM DASS (*Fading on*): Here is the child, Sahib.

SARA (*Fading on*): Your monkey ran away, Sir, and I would have brought him back last night, but I knew you were ill and thought you might not like to be disturbed so late.

MR. CARRISFORD: That was very thoughtful of you, child.

SARA: Shall I give him to the Lascar?

MR. CARRISFORD: How do you know that Ram Dass is a Lascar?

SARA: Oh, I know Lascars. I was born in India!

MR. CARRISFORD (*Excitedly*): You were born in India, were you? Come here. You live next door?

SARA: Yes, I live at Miss Minchin's Seminary.

MR. CARMICHAEL: But you are not one of the pupils?

SARA: I don't think I know exactly *what* I am.

MR. CARRISFORD: Why not?

SARA: At first, I was a regular boarder, but now I sleep in the attic. I run errands for the cook, and I teach the little ones their lessons.

MR. CARRISFORD: (*Weakly*): Question her, Carmichael. I cannot.

MR. CARMICHAEL: What do you mean by "at first," my child?

SARA: When I was first brought there by my papa. But he died. He lost all his money, and there was none left for me. There was no one to take care of me or to pay Miss Minchin.

MR. CARRISFORD (*Excitedly*): Carmichael!

MR. CARMICHAEL: How did your father lose his money, my dear?

SARA: He did not lose it himself. He had a friend he was very fond of. It was his friend who lost the money; he trusted his friend too much.

MR. CARRISFORD: Perhaps it was a mistake. The friend might have *meant* to do no harm.

SARA: The suffering was just as bad for my poor papa. It killed him.

MR. CARRISFORD: What was your father's name? Tell me.

SARA: His name was Ralph Crewe, Captain Crewe. He died in India.

MR. CARRISFORD: Carmichael—it is the child! The child!

SARA (*Puzzled*): What child am I?

MR. CARMICHAEL: Mr. Carrisford here was your father's friend. We have been looking for you for two years, Sara Crewe.

SARA: And I was at Miss Minchin's all the while, just on the other side of the wall!

MR. CARMICHAEL: Mr. Carrisford did not know that. We thought you were in Europe. When he saw you pass by his house when you were doing errands for Miss Minchin, he did not dream you were Sara Crewe. Still, when Ram Dass told Mr. Carrisford about you, Mr. Carrisford felt very sorry for you and told Ram Dass to buy you books and blankets and other things to try to make you more comfortable.

SARA (*Happily*): Did Ram Dass bring all of those wonderful things? Then, Mr. Carrisford, *you* have been my friend all the time I have been poor.

MR. CARRISFORD: You are poor no longer, Sara, my dear. The diamond mines are in full operation, and you are a very rich little girl.

RAM DASS (*Fading on*): Sahib, a woman is here to see you.

MISS MINCHIN (*Fading on*): I am sorry to disturb you, Mr. Carrisford. I am Miss Minchin, the proprietress of the Young Ladies' Seminary next door. I understand that one of my students has been so bold as to intrude upon your privacy—a charity pupil. I came to ask your forgiveness. Go home at once, Sara. You shall be severely punished.

MR. CARMICHAEL: Excuse me, Miss Minchin, but Sara is not going.

MISS MINCHIN: Not going!

MR. CARMICHAEL: No. Mr. Carrisford was an intimate friend of her late father, Captain Crewe. The fortune which Captain Crewe supposed he had lost is in Mr. Carrisford's hands.

MISS MINCHIN: The fortune!

MR. CARMICHAEL: It will be Sara's fortune. In fact, it is Sara's fortune now.

MISS MINCHIN: Captain Crewe left her in my charge. She must return to my seminary until she is of age. The law will intercede in my behalf!

MR. CARRISFORD: The law will do no such thing.

MISS MINCHIN: Then I appeal to you, Sara. I have not spoiled you, perhaps, but you know your papa was pleased with your progress. Wouldn't you like to return to the seminary, as a regular parlor boarder? You know I have always been fond of you, Sara.

SARA (*Calmly*): Have you, Miss Minchin? I did not know that. You know why I will not go home with you, Miss Minchin. You know quite well.

MISS MINCHIN: I see. Mr. Carrisford, I will send you my bill tomorrow. I shall get some reward out of the diamond mines yet! And you will soon discover, sir, that Sara is neither truthful nor grateful. I suppose, Sara, that you now feel yourself a princess again?

SARA: I tried not to be anything else, Miss Minchin. Even when I was coldest and hungriest, I *tried* not to be.

MR. CARRISFORD: Now it will no longer be necessary for

you to try, my dear. You will have a comfortable home here with me always and everything your heart desires. I shall see to it that Miss Minchin allows any of your friends to come and visit with you whenever you like.

SARA: Oh, Mr. Carrisford, I'm *so* glad that it was you who were my friend.

MR. CARRISFORD: You will have many friends from now on, my dear. You have become a little princess. You will have many friends indeed, Sara Crewe.

MUSIC: *Happy theme, in and under.*

THE END

Sherlock Holmes and the Stockbroker's Clerk

Sherlock Holmes and the Stockbroker's Clerk

by A. Conan Doyle

Characters

DR. WATSON	ARTHUR PINNER ⎱ *played by a single*
SHERLOCK HOLMES	HARRY PINNER ⎰ *actor*
HALL PYCROFT	PORTER
	NEWSBOY

WATSON: Most men, when they get married, retire from the world for a little while, and allow their lives to become circumscribed by the four walls of their homes. But most men do not have an intimate acquaintance with the master detective, Sherlock Holmes. Therefore, I cannot admit to much surprise when, three weeks after my wedding, the bell of my town house door was rung, and I opened it to find my good friend, Sherlock Holmes.

SOUND: *Doorbell, followed by a brief pause, then sound of door being opened.*

HOLMES: My dear Watson, I am truly delighted to see you.

WATSON (*Gaily*): Sherlock Holmes, you old dog! Come in, come in!

HOLMES: I trust that Mrs. Watson has entirely recovered

119

from all the little excitements connected with our adventure of the Sign of Four?

WATSON: Thank you, we are both well.

HOLMES: And I hope that the cares of your medical practice, coupled with the joys of marriage, have not served to dampen the interest which you used to take in our little deductive problems.

WATSON: On the contrary, it was only last night that I was discussing them with Mrs. Watson. That sad business of Pondicherry Lodge, for instance—and the curious mystery of the Beryl Coronet. I wouldn't mind seeing another case like that one.

HOLMES: Then you don't consider your collection closed?

WATSON: Not at all. I should wish nothing better than to have some more such experiences.

HOLMES: Today, for example? Even though you have not been well lately?

WATSON (*Taken aback*): How did you ever know that, Holmes?

HOLMES: You know my methods, my dear Watson. I deduced it.

WATSON: But from what?

HOLMES: From your slippers.

WATSON: How on earth—?

HOLMES: Your slippers are new. You could not have had them more than a few weeks—bought them for your wedding trip, I'd say. And yet the soles of them are slightly scorched. For a moment I thought they might have been wet and then burned in the drying. But near the instep there is a small disc of paper with the shopman's marks on it. The damp would of course have removed this. You had, then, been sitting with your feet outstretched to the fire, which a man would hardly do in the middle of June if he were in full health.

WATSON: You never cease to amaze me, Holmes. It's incredible!

HOLMES: On the contrary, my dear Watson, it's elementary. I am afraid that I rather give myself away when I explain. Results without reasons are so much more impressive. But come, let us get to the business at hand. I have a case in Birmingham today. Will you come?

WATSON: Certainly. What is the case?

HOLMES: My client will tell it all to you on the train on our way down. Can you come at once?

WATSON: In an instant. Let me just get my coat on and have a word with my wife.

HOLMES: Very good. I shall meet you outside your door. I have some instructions for the cab driver, and I wish to take advantage of a few extra minutes in the sun.

MUSIC: *Light theme, in and under. Out.*

WATSON: After telling my bride about the errand I was about to undertake, I donned my greatcoat and went out the door, to find Holmes standing on my step, breathing in the fresh June air.

SOUND: *Door closing.*

HOLMES: Ah, here you are, Watson. I have been looking around. I see your neighbor is a doctor, too.

WATSON: Yes, he bought an old practice just as I did. As a matter of fact, both our practices are of the same age —they have been here ever since the houses were built.

HOLMES: Ah! Then you got hold of the better of the two.

WATSON: I think I did. But how did you know?

HOLMES: By the steps, my boy. Yours are worn three inches deeper than his. But we chat too long. My client is in the cab waiting for us. Come along and I'll introduce you.

WATSON: With pleasure, Holmes.

SOUND: *Cab door being slammed.*

HOLMES: Dr. Watson, I should like to present to you a most interesting young man—Mr. Hall Pycroft.

MUSIC: *Light theme, in and under. Out.*

WATSON: The man whom I found myself facing was a well-built, fresh-complexioned young fellow, with a frank, honest face. He wore a neat suit of sober black, which made him look like what he was—a smart young city man, probably employed somewhere as a junior clerk. It was not until we were all in a first-class railway carriage and well started upon our journey to Birmingham, however, that I was able to learn what trouble had driven him to Sherlock Holmes.

SOUND: *Railroad wheels in softly in background and out.*

HOLMES: We have a clear run here of seventy minutes. I want you, Mr. Pycroft, to tell Dr. Watson your very interesting experience, exactly as you told it to me.

PYCROFT (*A pleasant-sounding young man*): With pleasure, Mr. Holmes.

HOLMES: It is a case, Watson, which may prove to have something in it. There are certainly some very unusual features. And I shall be glad of the chance to hear the story again, so that I may review some of the particulars for myself.

PYCROFT: Well, then. I used to be a clerk in a stockbroking firm. I'd been with them five years and was doing very well, when the firm was forced to close. They gave me very good recommendations, but that didn't help the fact that I was out of work. And so I began to look around. At last I saw a vacancy advertised at Mawson & Williams.

WATSON: The firm on Lombard Street? It's the richest in London.

PYCROFT: So it is, and I knew there'd be many, many applicants for the post. But even though I had little chance of getting it, I sent in my letter of application. And, believe it or not, back came a letter saying that if I would appear the next Monday, I might take over my new duties at once. The pay was better than I had been earning, and the duties were the same. You couldn't have found a happier man in London than I was when I got that position.

WATSON: I can well believe it.

PYCROFT: But now I come to the strange part of the business. I was living in a small boarding house in an out-of-the-way corner of London. It was more economical, you know, and my funds were somewhat depleted by my long siege of unemployment. I was sitting over my poor supper, thinking about my luck (*Fading*), when the hall-porter brought in a card.

SOUND: *Knock on door, door being opened.*

PORTER: Mr. Pycroft? There's a gentleman below-stairs to see you, sir. Sent up this card.

PYCROFT: A gentleman to see me? But nobody knows I live here. Let me see the card. Hm-m. "Arthur Pinner, Financial Agent." I don't know him. But still—why not? Show him up.

PORTER: Very good, sir.

PYCROFT (*Musing*): I wonder how on earth the fellow knows me. What does he want of me? And how did he find me?

PORTER (*Off mike, announcing*): Mr. Arthur Pinner, sir.

PINNER (*A sly, older man, fading on*): Mr. Hall Pycroft, I believe?

PYCROFT: Yes, sir. Please come in.

SOUND: *Door closing*.

PINNER: You were lately engaged at Coxon & Woodhouse's and are now to be on the staff of Mawson's?

PYCROFT: Quite so. You seem to know a good deal about me, sir.

PINNER: Well, the fact is that I have heard some really extraordinary stories about your financial ability. You remember Parker, who used to be manager at Coxon's? He can never praise you enough. Among your strong points, I believe, is a good memory, is it not?

PYCROFT: It's pretty fair, I must admit.

PINNER: You don't mind if I test you on that point, do you? I'm sure you read the stock quotations each day. What is the price of Ayrshires?

PYCROFT (*Promptly*): A hundred and six and a quarter to a hundred and five and seven-eighths.

PINNER: And New Zealand Consolidated?

PYCROFT: A hundred and four.

PINNER: British Broken Hills.

PYCROFT: Seven to seven-and-six.

PINNER: Wonderful! This quite fits in with all I have heard. My boy, you are much too good to be a clerk at Mawson's.

PYCROFT: I am very glad to have a position at Mawson's.

PINNER: Oh, pooh, man, you should be doing far better. Now I'll tell you how it is with me. What I have to offer is little enough for a man of your ability, but compared to Mawson's offer, it's a fortune. When do you start at Mawson's?

PYCROFT: On Monday.

PINNER (*Laughing*): I'll wager you'll never go there at all. By Monday you will be the business manager of the Franco-Midland Hardware Company, Limited, with a hundred and thirty-four branches all over France, not counting one in Brussels and one in San Remo.

PYCROFT: But—I've never heard of it!

PINNER: I daresay you haven't. It has been kept very quiet, because we don't want the word to get around until we have already started our operations in England. The competition, you know. Now, my brother—Harry Pinner—is managing director; he has asked me to find a good man to be business manager. I've heard a good deal about you, and have decided that you're the man for me —although we're prepared to offer you only five hundred pounds a year to start.

PYCROFT (*Amazed*): Five—five hundred pounds! But that's four times what Mawson's giving me.

PINNER: You're worth more, my boy. What do you say to my offer?

PYCROFT: It's quite handsome, indeed, Mr. Pinner. But I must be frank. Mawson may not pay so handsomely, but it is a safe, secure company. I know so little about your company.

PINNER: Smart, smart. You are the very man for us. You are not to be talked over; I like that. Now, to answer your question, here's a hundred pounds for you, as an advance against your salary. That's security, isn't it?

PYCROFT (*Firmly*): You have just hired yourself a business

manager, Mr. Pinner. When shall I take over my duties?

PINNER: Be in Birmingham tomorrow at one. I have a note in my pocket which you will take to my brother, Harry Pinner. You will find him at this address, where the temporary offices of the company are located. He will explain your duties.

PYCROFT: Really, sir, I hardly know how to express my gratitude.

PINNER: Not at all, my boy. But there are one or two small things—mere formalities—which must be arranged. You have a bit of paper beside you there. Kindly write upon it: "I am perfectly willing to act as business manager of the Franco-Midland Hardware Company, Limited, at a minimum salary of five hundred pounds."

SOUND: *Pen writing on paper.*

PYCROFT (*Slowly*): "Minimum—salary, five—hundred—pounds." There you are.

PINNER: And one last thing. What do you intend to do about Mawson's?

PYCROFT: I declare, I'd forgotten about them. I'll write and resign.

PINNER: Precisely what I don't want you to do. I had a row with Mawson's manager over you. I told him I was interested in you and he was quite offensive; said that as he had hired you first, you'd no right to consider any other offer, no matter how much to your advantage. As a matter of fact, do you know what he said about you? "We picked Pycroft out of the gutter, and he's too grateful to us not to come to work here, no matter what you pay."

PYCROFT: The impudence!

PINNER: Those were his very words. Don't you think it would serve him right to give him no notice at all?

PYCROFT: Imagine his talking about me like that—when I've never set eyes on him in my life. I shall certainly not write if you would rather I didn't.

PINNER: Good! That's a promise! Well, Mr. Pycroft, I'm delighted with our business transaction. We have a good man in you. Now don't forget to be in Birmingham tomorrow at one o'clock sharp, and present this letter to my brother. He'll be expecting you. I must be off now, but we shall meet again.

PYCROFT: Thank you, Mr. Pinner. I'm eternally grateful, you can be sure.

PINNER: Never you mind. *I'm* the one who is grateful. Goodbye now, and good luck. (*Fading*) May you have all the fortune that you deserve!

MUSIC: *Lively theme, up and out.*

WATSON: And was that the entire interview before you took your new position?

PYCROFT: That is just about all that passed between us, as near as I can remember. You can imagine, Dr. Watson, how pleased I was at such an extraordinary bit of luck. I sat up half the night thinking about it, and the next day I was off to Birmingham. After settling in a hotel, I made my way straight to the address that had been given me.

WATSON: And what sort of offices did you find?

PYCROFT: That was the first thing that startled me. When I got to the building, I looked for the company name on the directory-board in the lobby, but it was not to be found.

WATSON: How curious!

PYCROFT: I stood for a moment with my heart in my boots, wondering whether the whole thing was an elaborate hoax, when someone suddenly addressed me. I looked up, and there before me was a man very like the chap I had seen the night before. He was the same size, with the same voice, but he was clean-shaven, and his hair was of a lighter color. Clearly, the men were brothers. (*Fading*) If it hadn't been for the hair, one might have said they were twins.

HARRY (*Fading on*): Are you Mr. Hall Pycroft? (*Note:* HARRY *is played by the same actor who plays* ARTHUR PINNER.)

PYCROFT: Yes, sir, I am.

HARRY: I was expecting you, but you are a trifle before your time. I had a note from my brother this morning in which he sings your praises!

PYCROFT: I was just looking for the offices when you came.

HARRY: We have not put our name up yet, for we only secured these temporary premises last week. (*Fading*) Come up with me, and we'll talk the whole thing over.

MUSIC: *Mysterious theme, in and under.*

PYCROFT: I followed him to the top of a lofty staircase, and there, right under the roof, were two empty, dusty little rooms, uncurtained and uncarpeted. I had imagined a great office with shining tables and rows of clerks, such as I was used to, and I daresay I rather stared at the two rickety chairs and one little table which, with a ledger, made up the whole furniture.

MUSIC: *Out.*

HARRY (*Jovially*): Come, Mr. Pycroft, don't be disheartened by humble appearances. Rome was not built in a day, and we have lots of money behind us, though we don't make much of a show with it. Pray sit down. From what my brother has written me of you, I know that you are the man we want. You may consider yourself definitely engaged.

PYCROFT: What are my duties to be, Mr. Pinner?

HARRY: You will eventually manage the great depot in Paris, which will pour a flood of English crockery into the shops of a hundred and thirty-four agents in France. The purchases will be completed in a week. Meanwhile you will remain here in Birmingham and make yourself useful.

PYCROFT: How?

HARRY: Here is a directory of Paris, with the trades listed after the names of the people. I want you to take it home with you and mark off all the hardware sellers, with their addresses. It would be of the greatest use to me to have them.

PYCROFT: But surely, sir, there are classified lists available?

HARRY: Not reliable ones. Their system is different from ours. Stick at it, and let me have the lists by Monday at twelve. If you continue to show zeal and intelligence, you will find us a good company. Good day, Mr. Pycroft.

MUSIC: *In and under. Fades out.*

PYCROFT: Well, gentlemen, what was I to think? The dingy offices—the lack of furniture—the absence of the company name upon the directory-board—all of these gave rise to my suspicions. And yet, Mr. Pinner had offered a good explanation for everything. Even the task he had set me to seemed reasonable, and so I gave it a try. All Sunday I was kept hard at work, and yet by Monday I had got only as far as the letter H. I went round to Mr. Pinner, found him in the same dismantled room, and was told to keep at it until Wednesday. On Wednesday it was still unfinished, so I hammered away until Friday

—that is, yesterday. (*Fading*) Then I brought it round to Mr. Harry Pinner. (*Pause*)

HARRY (*Fading on*): Thank you very much, Mr. Pycroft. I fear that I underrated the difficulty of the task. This list will be of very material assistance to me.

PYCROFT: It took some time.

HARRY: And now I want you to make a list of the furniture shops, for they all sell crockery.

PYCROFT: Very good, sir, if that is what you want.

HARRY: And you can come up tomorrow evening at seven, and let me know how you are getting on. But don't over-work yourself, my boy. A couple of hours at a music hall in the evening would do you a world of good. (*Laughs evilly*) Yes, yes, Mr. Pycroft. Take your time. (*Fading*) There's no hurry. By all means take your time.

MUSIC: *Mysterious theme. Up and out.*

PYCROFT: And that, Dr. Watson, is the whole story.

WATSON: And you think there is some mystery in the business? It all sounds perfectly legitimate and straight-forward to me.

HOLMES: But that is because Mr. Pycroft neglected to tell you one interesting thing which he observed—a thing of a most peculiar nature.

PYCROFT: By George, I did leave that out.

WATSON: What is it, man?

PYCROFT: As Mr. Harry Pinner discharged me last evening, he laughed—as I told you. And I saw that his second tooth upon the left-hand side had been very badly filled with gold.

WATSON: And is that all? That doesn't sound like much to me.

PYCROFT: You are quite right, Dr. Watson. There's much

more to it. When I was speaking to the other chap in London—Mr. *Arthur* Pinner—I happened to notice that his same tooth was filled in the identical fashion. Of course you expect that two brothers will resemble each other, but not that they will have the same tooth filled in the same way. And then it suddenly occurred to me that the only differences in their appearances were such things as might be quickly altered with a razor and with dye. The things that *can't* be quickly changed—the voice, the figure, the teeth, the eyes—those were the same.

HOLMES: An excellent observation, you will agree, Watson.

WATSON: But if both men were the same, what is the meaning of it? Why had he sent you from London to Birmingham? Why had he gone there early to meet you? And why had he written a letter from himself to himself?

PYCROFT: Those are the very questions I asked myself, Dr. Watson. And because I could not answer them, I went to the one man in all of England who could help me find the answers. That is precisely why I have called upon your good friend, Sherlock Holmes.

MUSIC: *In, under, and out.*

WATSON: I confess that I found Mr. Pycroft's story interesting, but it was not until he mentioned the detail of the gold tooth that I perceived the mystery in the affair. Now, however, I could understand why Holmes had shown such enthusiasm for the case. The train had pulled into Birmingham Station just as Pycroft finished his narrative, and the three of us climbed down onto the platform. Both the young stockbroker's clerk and I turned upon Holmes with eager anticipation, anxious to know how he intended to proceed with the business.

HOLMES (*Delightedly*): Rather fine, Watson, is it not? There are points in it which please me. I think you will agree with me that an interview with Mr. Arthur Harry Pinner—for we must call him by both names until we discover who he really is—in the temporary offices of the Franco-Midland Hardware Company, Limited, would be a rather interesting experience for both of us.

WATSON: But how can we manage it without his suspecting who we are?

PYCROFT: Oh, easily enough. You can pretend to be two friends of mine who are in need of jobs. What could be more natural than that I should bring you both around to the managing director of my company?

HOLMES: Quite so, quite so. I should like to have a look at the gentleman, and see if I can make anything of his little game. I can't help but wonder, Mr. Pycroft, what it is about you that should have attracted him.

WATSON: Shall we go right over to the offices now?

PYCROFT: There is no use in that. He comes there only to see me, apparently, for the place is deserted up to the very hour he names.

HOLMES: That is certainly suggestive of mischief.

PYCROFT (*Suddenly*): I say! We are in luck. There he is ahead of us—the very man!

WATSON: Which one? Where?

PYCROFT: That one there, with his head lowered. He must have come down on the same train as we did.

HOLMES: He's probably on his way to keep his appointment with you now, Mr. Pycroft. At least we will not be disappointed. I find myself quite anxious to have a good, long look at Mr. Arthur Harry Pinner.

MUSIC: *Mysterious theme, in, under and out.*

WATSON: The man Pycroft had pointed to was a smallish, well-dressed fellow, who seemed quite intent upon his own thoughts, for he never once looked up, but went bustling along the streets with firm determination. Following him at a short distance, Holmes, Pycroft, and I never lost sight of him, and soon we found ourselves walking down the street of the company's offices. At the corner, there was a young urchin selling newspapers. (*Pause*)

NEWSBOY (*Off mike*): All the London papers here! Get your evening papers here!

HARRY (*Off mike*): Here boy. A *Standard*—and be quick about it! (*Pause*)

WATSON: Pinner threw the boy a coin, and clutching his newspaper tightly, he bustled off into the company's building, a worried look on his face. Following Pycroft's lead, we entered the same doorway, and after climbing five flights of stairs, found ourselves outside a half-opened door, at which our client tapped. We entered a bare, unfurnished room such as had been described to us. At the single table sat the man whom we had seen in the street, with his evening paper spread in front of him, and as he looked up, I saw an expression of grief, torment, and horror. His brow glistened with perspiration, his cheeks were dead white, his eyes glazed. He looked at his clerk as though he did not recognize him, so preoccupied was he with his own terrible thoughts.

PYCROFT: You look ill, Mr. Pinner!

HARRY (*Abstractedly, almost wildly*): Yes, I—I am not very well. Who are these gentlemen?

PYCROFT: They are friends of mine, who are in need of work. I thought you might be able to make use of their experience in your enterprise.

HARRY: Yes—yes—possibly, quite possibly. But I cannot talk about it now—I—please, please, leave me alone for a little bit. I—I must be alone.

PYCROFT: You forget, Mr. Pinner, that I am here by appointment.

HARRY: Appointment? Yes—yes, of course. I beg your pardon. You may wait here. You may all wait here. I must just slip away—if you will excuse me, I must go into the next room, only—only for a moment. *(Fading)* Excuse me—just for a moment. I—I must be alone—just for a moment.

SOUND: *Door closing, off mike.*

HOLMES: Is he trying to give us the slip?

PYCROFT: It's impossible. There's no door in that second room except the one he entered by. It's an inside room —not so much as a window in it.

HOLMES: Is it furnished?

PYCROFT: It wasn't yesterday.

WATSON: Then what on earth can he be doing in there? Probably went in merely to recover his composure. He did seem awfully upset. I say—do you suppose he suspects we are detectives? Is that what's upset him?

HOLMES: No. He was already upset when we came in.

SOUND: *Moans off mike.*

PYCROFT: What's that?

HOLMES: It's Pinner. See what he's up to.

SOUND: *Footsteps running, then door being opened.*

PYCROFT: Good grief!

HOLMES: He's—he's hanged himself. How is he, Watson?

WATSON: Dead, by Jove. He's made a good job of it. Dead as a doornail.

HOLMES (*Regretfully*): I suppose we ought to call the police in. And yet I confess that I'd like to give them a complete case when they come.

PYCROFT: It's a blessed mystery to me. Whatever did he want to bring me all the way up here for, when he—

HOLMES (*Interrupting*): Pooh! All that is clear enough. It is just this last sudden move that has me confused.

WATSON (*Incredulous*): You understand the rest, then? I must confess that I am out of my depth.

HOLMES: Surely if you consider the events at first, they can only point to one conclusion. The whole thing hinges upon two points. The first is that he made Pycroft write a declaration by which he entered the services of this preposterous company. Do you not see how very suggestive it is?

WATSON: No, I'm afraid I don't.

HOLMES: Why did they want him to do it? It's not a usual business practice, you know. The only reason is that they were anxious to obtain a specimen of our young friend's handwriting.

PYCROFT: But why should they need my handwriting?

HOLMES: There can be only one adequate reason. Someone wished to learn to imitate it. And for the explanation of why, we must consider the second point: that you were specifically requested not to resign your position at Mawson's, but to leave the manager there under the expectation that Mr. Hall Pycroft, whom he had never seen, was about to enter the office upon the next Monday morning.

PYCROFT: Of course! What a blind fool I've been!

HOLMES: Suppose that someone turned up in your place, writing in a hand identical to that in which your letter of application was written. How easy it would be for him to pass himself off as you. Of course, it was of the utmost importance to persuade you to accept the fake job offer, for it was essential that an impostor go to Mawson's in your place. That is why you were given the magnificent sum of a hundred pounds in advance; they wanted to make sure of you. And, of course, they very cleverly arranged for you to leave London, so that there would be no chance of your showing up at Mawson's on any pretext.

PYCROFT: But why should this man pretend to have been his brother?

HOLMES: That is pretty clear, also. There are evidently only two of them in on the scheme—whatever scheme it is. The other is impersonating you at the office. This one acted as your engager, and then found that it was wiser to pretend to be your Birmingham employer as well, rather than admit a third person into the plot. He changed his appearance and passed himself off as his own brother. But for the happy accident of the gold tooth, he would have succeeded.

PYCROFT: But what scheme were they working? Why should one of them want to gain entrance to Mawson's under false pretenses?

WATSON: And why should the other hang himself the minute we walk into the room?

HOLMES: That is what I do not yet understand. (*Suddenly*) The paper! Of course! I should have thought of it before. The secret must lie there.

PYCROFT: Here is the newspaper Pinner was reading. What do you make of it?

SOUND: *Rustling newspaper pages.*

HOLMES: It's an early edition of the *Evening Standard.* Let me see. Hm-m . . . hmm. Aha, here it is. Look at this, Watson, and tell us what you think.

WATSON: Ah! Listen to the headline of this story. "Murder at Mawson & Williams. Gigantic Robbery Attempted. Capture of the Criminal."

PYCROFT: I begin to understand.

HOLMES: By pretending to be you, the criminal managed to gain access to the safe. I gather from the newspaper that he was discovered by a guard, whom he killed. But fortunately the police caught him in time. And this fellow, when he learned that the jig was up, decided to kill himself.

WATSON: Yes, Holmes, listen to this. "The criminal is lodged in Holloway Gaol. His brother, however, who usually works with him, has not appeared in this job as far as we can presently ascertain, although the police are making energetic enquiries as to his whereabouts."

HOLMES: Well, we may save the police some little trouble in that direction.

PYCROFT: It's ironic, isn't it? To think that this fellow really had a brother in London after all!

WATSON: I must congratulate you, Holmes, on your splendid deductions.

HOLMES: You could have done the same, Watson.

WATSON: I disagree. You have pieced the thing together with uncanny skill. I don't know how you do it. It's amazing!

HOLMES: On the contrary. It's elementary, my dear Watson. Elementary!

MUSIC: *Full to finish.*

THE END

The Iliad

The Iliad

by Homer

Characters

TWO MESSENGERS	ODYSSEUS
AGAMEMNON	AJAX
ACHILLES	PATROCLUS
HECTOR	KING PRIAM
DIOMEDES	NARRATOR

NARRATOR: Helen of Sparta was one of the most beautiful women of the ancient world. Because of her beauty, Paris, handsome young prince of Troy, carried her off with the help of the goddess Aphrodite. When Helen's husband, King Menelaus of Sparta, learned of her abduction, he called together all the chieftains of Greece to help him win Helen back. A thousand ships were launched, and the Trojan War—one of the most heroic and most heartbreaking wars of history—was begun. Though the war was fought thousands of years ago, even today men still enjoy reading about it, for the story of the war between the Trojans and the Greeks was magnificently set down in an epic poem by the most famous minstrel of all time, Homer. Here, then, is the story of the Trojan War: *The Iliad,* by Homer.

MUSIC: *Exciting theme, up and out.*

NARRATOR: For nine long years the battle between Greece and Troy has been raging. Men have almost forgotten the cause of the war. But on they fight, each soldier valiantly determined that the war will not end until either Troy or Greece has been completely destroyed by her enemies. Even the gods themselves have taken sides in this long and bitter war, and month after month after month goes by with first one side gaining an advantage, only to lose it again to the other. And in both camps, the lists of the dead and the dying become longer and longer. But still, the battle rages. Our story begins in the camp of the Greeks, outside the walls of Troy, at the end of the ninth long year of war. In the tent of King Agamemnon, the Greek generals receive a messenger.

FIRST MESSENGER: Hear me, oh King Agamemnon!

AGAMEMNON: Speak, messenger. Good news, I hope! I, Agamemnon, hear you.

MESSENGER: In yesterday's battle, King Agamemnon, a prisoner was taken—a girl, named Chryseis.

AGAMEMNON (*Laughing*): Why do you tell this to me? Who should know of Chryseis' capture better than I? Was she not awarded to me as a prize, to be my personal slave?

MESSENGER: But do you know who she is, King Agamemnon?

AGAMEMNON: If you mean by that, do I know the names of her father and mother, I do not. And I do not care to know them! She is of the enemy, is she not? Therefore, it is meet and just that she should be my slave.

MESSENGER: But, sire, her father is a priest of Apollo!

AGAMEMNON: What's that to me? The gods are on the side of the Greeks in this war. What do I care if her father *does* pray to Apollo? He will not listen to such prayers.

MESSENGER: But, sire . . .

AGAMEMNON: Enough! I will hear no more.

ACHILLES: Do not be a fool, Agamemnon. Listen to what the messenger has to say. It may be important!

AGAMEMNON (*Proudly*): Do you give *me* advice, Achilles? Remember who I am.

ACHILLES: I know you are King. But in a matter of war, that does not matter. Am I not a general? Listen to the messenger!

AGAMEMNON: Very well, Achilles. You may speak, messenger.

MESSENGER: This girl's father—this priest of Apollo—has brought a curse upon our men. Even now the men in our camp lie stricken with disease. None is expected to live, and already the funeral fires are being built. Apollo is angry; he will not stop this disease until the girl is returned!

AGAMEMNON (*Angrily*): What? For myself, I would not give up this slave. But if it be Apollo's will, I see I must —for the good of the men.

ACHILLES: Wisely spoken, Agamemnon!

AGAMEMNON: Thank me not too quickly, Achilles. I shall give up this female slave . . . but I insist on having another in her place. I am a king and should be served. Therefore, you must give me the slave that was awarded as a prize to you, Achilles.

ACHILLES: That is not fair!

AGAMEMNON: Is it fair that I, Agamemnon, should make all the sacrifices? (*Calling out*) Guards! Go to the tent of

Achilles, and fetch me his captured slave!

ACHILLES: No!

AGAMEMNON: Your men will not dare stop mine, Achilles. They, at least, know enough to show respect to me!

ACHILLES (*Contemptuously*): You selfish man! You care more for your own rank than for harmony among your generals! Very well! I cannot stop this insult. But I shall bear no more. I shall take my ships, and all my men, and let you try to do without me! You can do all your own fighting from now on.

AGAMEMNON: Go ahead, Achilles. I do not need your help!

ACHILLES: The time will come, Agamemnon, when you will beat your breast, and tear your hair, and weep like a woman that ever you did send me away. Your men will fall by the thousands, like wheat before the reapers, and you will curse in sorrow the day when you insulted the best of all men, Achilles.

MUSIC: *Dramatic theme, up full and out.*

NARRATOR: Thus, the selfishness of one Greek leader and the anger of another brings about a rift in the army. Fulfilling his threat, Achilles withdraws his men from the battle, and sails with them out of the harbor of Troy, anchoring his fleet where he can readily receive news of the battle. But to add further to his vengeance, Achilles prays a fierce prayer to Zeus, father of the gods.

ACHILLES: Father Zeus, most powerful and greatest of all the gods, wisest of all the gods and best, hear this, the prayer of your humble servant, Achilles. Let the favor of the war go to the enemies of Agamemnon, to the Trojans. Let Agamemnon's losses be great, his defeats many. Fling the Greeks back to their ships with direful carnage, until they pay me, the great Achilles, the honor that is my due.

MUSIC: *Dramatic theme, up full and out.*

NARRATOR: As Achilles is one of Zeus' best-loved, the great god listens to his prayer, and that night sends a false dream to Agamemnon, who lies sleeping in his tent. It is a dream of great victory for the Greeks, and Agamemnon, not knowing that the dream is a trick of the gods, believes it is a good omen.

AGAMEMNON: My soldiers, last night I had a dream which is a certain sign that soon great Troy will be ours. Even King Priam and Queen Hecuba, our hated enemies, will bow their heads in defeat before you, my glorious heroes of Greece. Arm yourselves well, and prepare yourselves fully. Today we will fight until all of Troy is burned, and all her men are slaughtered in the fields. Come, my soldiers! I have had a dream from the gods, and victory is ours!

MUSIC: *Tense theme, in and under. Out.*

NARRATOR: And so, influenced by his false dream, Agamemnon leads his men into battle at the break of day. But in answer to the prayer of Achilles, Zeus gives the victory to the Trojans. With Hector, the valiant son of King Priam of Troy, as their captain, the Trojans fight as they have never fought before, and the troops of Agamemnon are scattered. On and on the brave Hector urges his men, calling out to them in the very thick of battle.

HECTOR: Trojans! Brave Trojans! Fight on! The Greeks are no match for us! See, we are forcing them to their ships! Drive them on! Let no man of the enemy live to report our victory. Drive them on!

Music: *Dramatic theme, up full and out.*

NARRATOR: And so, with victory in their hands, the Trojans drive the Greeks back to their tents and ships. But before the victory can become completely theirs, night falls, and the Trojans are forced to return to their city, leaving Agamemnon's men to mourn their losses and bury their dead. That night, Agamemnon meets sorrowfully with the other Greek leaders, to make plans for the next day.

AGAMEMNON: My generals, the gods have, at last, turned their backs upon our prayers and our cause. We are defeated.

DIOMEDES: But, Agamemnon, did you not dream that Zeus would give us the victory?

AGAMEMNON: Ah, Diomedes, I see now, though it is too late, that the dream was a false dream, and that great Zeus is on the side of our enemies, the Trojans.

ODYSSEUS: What do you mean to do, Agamemnon?

AGAMEMNON: What *can* I do, brave Odysseus? The war is over. To remain and try to fight would be foolhardy. The Trojans will only kill our men and burn our ships.

AJAX: Do you mean, then, to turn back, Agamemnon?

AGAMEMNON: Yes, Ajax, I mean to turn back. If it be the will of the gods that the victory be Troy's, let us set sail in defeat for Argos while we are still able to, for surely we will never conquer Troy, and if we remain, Hector's men will kill those of us who still live.

DIOMEDES: My lord . . .

AGAMEMNON: Yes, Diomedes?

DIOMEDES: Your advice is foolish, and your plan the plan of a coward!

AGAMEMNON (*Outraged*): You speak thus to me? To me, King Agamemnon?

DIOMEDES: The time for foolish pride and ceremony is over. What if you are King? You are a coward, just the same. Go! Take your men and your fleet back to Mycenae. Save your own neck, and sacrifice your manliness!

AGAMEMNON: Do you want to stay and be slaughtered, Diomedes?

DIOMEDES: I want to stay and fight to the finish. Even if you go back—all of you—Agamemnon, Ajax, Odysseus, all—I intend to stay and do my best, until the will of the gods prevail and I either conquer or fall!

ODYSSEUS: Well spoken, Diomedes!

AJAX: Diomedes is right. Are we cowards—or men?

ALL: Not cowards! Men!

AJAX: Diomedes has given us good advice, and that is what we need most.

AGAMEMNON: If you are all agreed that we should stand and fight, then I shall stay also.

ODYSSEUS: You will not regret doing so, Agamemnon.

DIOMEDES: Agamemnon, there is yet one thing which you can do for us—and which only you can do—a service that would render great benefit to the cause of the Greeks.

AGAMEMNON: Name it, Diomedes.

DIOMEDES: Send for Achilles, and for his friend, Patroclus. Tell Achilles that you need him, and apologize for your foolish quarrel with him. If Achilles will return to our side, we may yet win the battle.

AGAMEMNON: You are right, Diomedes. I see now what a fool I was to insult him, and let him leave in anger.

AJAX: But will Achilles return?

AGAMEMNON: If I can humble myself and apologize to him, I know he will unbend and forgive me for my insult. Go you, Odysseus, and Ajax, go you with him. Go to Achilles. Tell him that I ask his forgiveness and his help. Bring him the finest gifts my tent contains, and ask him to return.

DIOMEDES: He will come back, and the victory will be ours!

AGAMEMNON: I was mad, indeed, ever to have let him depart. A man so loved of the gods is worth an army of others. Go, Ajax and Odysseus. Go to Achilles!

MUSIC: *Tense theme, in and under. Out.*

NARRATOR: So the two messengers from Agamemnon, Ajax and Odysseus, set sail for the harbor where the ships of Achilles are anchored. When they board Achilles' ship, he and his dear friend Patroclus greet them.

ACHILLES: How now, Odysseus? Welcome, Ajax! Is the war newly won? Do you bring me news?

AJAX: We bring you news indeed, Achilles, but not of the war's end.

ODYSSEUS: The war rages still, more fiercely than ever before.

PATROCLUS: Which side have the gods favored?

ODYSSEUS: The Trojans seem to be the favored of the gods, Patroclus. We, and the others of our camp, have suffered great losses. Even now, the fighting goes on by the shore of the sea.

ACHILLES: Why do you come here to bring this news to me? Patroclus and I are not interested in the Trojan war.

AJAX: Achilles, our business with you is not simply to

bear news of the battle. It is more urgent business—
business of life and death. You must come back to the
battle and help us, Achilles—or we die.

ACHILLES: I vowed that I would not return to the battle.

ODYSSEUS: You must! Only you and your men can save the
lives of our people—your people.

AJAX: You are proud, Achilles, but this is no time for
pride. Agamemnon begs your forgiveness, admits his
wrongs to you, offers bounteous gifts and great wealth
to you, and humbly asks that you return.

ACHILLES: I care nothing for Agamemnon's gifts! I am
tired of these years of bloodshed. Why must there be
war? Why can there be no peace? Life and liberty are
worth more than all the wealth in the world. Tell that
to your proud and foolish Agamemnon. I will not come.

ODYSSEUS: Agamemnon will be sorely grieved, Achilles.

ACHILLES: Then he is more of a fool than I thought. Farewell, gentlemen.

PATROCLUS: Wait, Ajax, and Odysseus!

AJAX: Yes, Patroclus?

PATROCLUS: I will come with you. Though I agree with
what Achilles has said, I still cannot desert my fellow
countrymen. And if you will have me fight with you,
then I am yours.

ODYSSEUS: Well spoken, Patroclus.

AJAX: Our troops will welcome you proudly.

PATROCLUS: Achilles, you are the dearest friend of my life.
Can you forgive my returning to the field?

ACHILLES: You are doing what you must do, Patroclus,
just as I am doing what I must do. Here, I give you my
own armor to wear. May it bring you good fortune,
and may the gods favor you in battle, dear friend. And

some day, when peace has been restored, may we find ourselves together in friendship again. Farewell, Patroclus.

PATROCLUS: Farewell, Achilles.

MUSIC: *Tense theme, up and out.*

NARRATOR: The next day, wearing Achilles' shining armor, Patroclus rides into the thick of battle. As if by magic, the fortune of the Greek army changes, and though the sun rose to find them huddling beside their fleet, as the day progresses the Greeks make greater and greater advances, till at last, under the leadership of Patroclus, they reach the very walls of Troy. There, the Trojan leader, brave Hector, challenges Patroclus to a duel, believing that Patroclus is really Achilles.

HECTOR: Stay, you murderous Achilles! Stand and fight! Many of my best soldiers have fallen at your hands today, and now you must answer to me for their blood!

PATROCLUS: You are as mistaken as you are rash, Hector. But your ghost shall follow theirs. Fight!

SOUND: *Clashing of swords. After a moment, body falling.*

HECTOR: Now, die, Achilles! Though the fates told me I would meet death at your hands, see how I have outwitted them!

PATROCLUS (*Gasping*): Be not too hasty, Hector. Though I wear the general's armor, I am but his friend, Patroclus. Though I die at your hands, Achilles lives yet . . . and therefore, Hector, *you* have not long to live!

MUSIC: *Unhappy theme, up and out.*

NARRATOR: So the noble Patroclus falls at the hands of the Trojan, Hector. When the news reaches Achilles, his grief is overwhelming.

ACHILLES: Oh, Patroclus, Patroclus, no man was ever your

match for honor, loyalty or valor. To see you dead makes me weep like a woman. I taste of tears now, which never have I drunk since childhood. How bitterly the gods answer our prayers. What matters it if all of Greece be vanquished, now that Patroclus is dead? I have no choice but to return to battle. Life is but emptiness, unless I am able to kill Hector with my own hand. They tell me Hector now wears my armor, stolen from Patroclus' corpse. It will not protect thee, Hector, for Achilles is fated to seal your death, and nothing can save you. An ancient oracle once told me that I should not live long after Hector died. If that be true, then let death come quickly . . . for Hector and for me.

MUSIC: *Tragic theme, up and out.*

NARRATOR: And thus, Achilles reverses his decision and sails into the city to do battle with the hated Trojans. The next day, a messenger approaches the throne room of Troy, carrying the news to King Priam and Prince Hector.

SECOND MESSENGER: Hector, Hector, Achilles fights before the walls of Troy.

HECTOR: Achilles! At last we shall see if I am indeed to fall before this famed Greek warrior.

SECOND MESSENGER: Already many have fallen beneath Achilles' sword. He—he has even killed—alas, I fear to name the victim. It is one of your own family.

PRIAM: Speak, messenger. Am I not the King of Troy?

SECOND MESSENGER (*Faltering*): Your Majesty . . . King Priam . . . Achilles has killed your youngest son, Polydoros.

PRIAM: Oh, woe, alas!

HECTOR: My brother Polydoros! Father, the time has come for me to kill this ruthless murderer, Achilles.

PRIAM: Stay, Hector! It is not fated that Achilles should die at your hands.

HECTOR: I must try my best, Father.

PRIAM: No, Hector, no! I am an old, old man. This war has brought me much agony and anguish. I can bear no more grief. Do not seek out Achilles, or I will never see you alive again. Have I lived to this age only to see all my sons slaughtered, my daughters taken in captivity as slaves? Who will tell the news to your mother, Queen Hecuba? Hector, my son, who will save Troy?

HECTOR: Father, as I am the general of the Trojan armies, I must do all I can to save our city. And so, I must do all I can to kill Achilles. If the gods will it, he will fall to me. If it be fated otherwise and I am to die today at his hands, then let it be so. I am not afraid, Father. Take you courage.

PRIAM: Hector, my son, if you die, what care I if Troy be victorious? If you live, what matters it if we be conquered by the Greeks? Hear me, Hector! I speak as your father.

HECTOR: Hear me, Father. You are a king! What must be, will be. Go in to my mother, the Queen, and pray with her.

MUSIC: *Unhappy theme, up and out.*

NARRATOR: And so it happens that Hector and Achilles, hated enemies, meet before the walls of Troy in mortal combat.

HECTOR: At last, Achilles, I meet you in the field—you of all men whom I have reason most to hate.

ACHILLES: I know your reason, Hector. The blood of

young Polydoros is newly spilled on my hands. But on your sword, the blood of my dear friend, Patroclus, is barely dry. Now, between us, let us see whom the gods love most dearly.

HECTOR: Gladly, Achilles. Let us fight, and let him fall who is least loved by Zeus. But first, I ask you to make me a promise.

ACHILLES: Speak, Hector, but make thy business brief.

HECTOR: If it be fated that the victory be mine, I swear to you no harm will befall your corpse. Your body will I give to your generals, that you may have fit burial and honor, according to your religion and your merit. I ask, in exchange, your oath to do the same by me, should I fall from favor of the gods today.

ACHILLES: We are not babes or women, Hector. We meet to fight, not to make words. There can be no compacts between us, no terms, no bargaining. Now draw your sword and fight. Prepare to die and lie in death as food for jackals.

HECTOR: So be it then. Draw thy sword.

SOUND: *Clashing swords.*

HECTOR (*Gasping*): I . . . I am hit. Death comes for me. Let me . . . at least . . . face it bravely.

ACHILLES (*Triumphantly*): Now, Prince Hector, pay for the death of worthy Patroclus. He shall be buried with all ceremony and honor while you shall lie to rot and feed the beasts of the field.

HECTOR (*Gasping*): Remember, Achilles . . . the fates have spoken . . . you cannot live long after I have died.

NARRATOR: As had been prophesied, Hector dies at the hands of Achilles, and when the news reaches King Priam, Hector's father, the old man's heart nearly breaks.

SECOND MESSENGER: He fought most valiantly, King Priam, but the gods willed that Achilles should win the victory. Your son is dead.

PRIAM (*In grief*): Oh, Hector, Hector!

SECOND MESSENGER: There is more, Your Majesty, though I am loathe to name it.

PRIAM: Speak. I think I am beyond all grief, all pain now.

SECOND MESSENGER: Achilles stripped proud Hector's body, throwing the silver armor to his men. He tied leather thongs to the feet of your son's corpse, and fastened them to his chariot, then galloped off to his own camp, at a furious pace, your son's proud body dragging along the ground.

PRIAM: Oh, it cannot be, it is not true!

SECOND MESSENGER: Too true, my lord.

PRIAM: Then will I go to Achilles' tent—aye, in the middle of the enemy camp. On my knees will I beg him for my son's body, that he may be buried with proper rites. I am an old king, and my pride is gone. I will go . . . and kneel before my enemy.

MUSIC: *Tragic theme, up and out.*

NARRATOR: So, humbling himself, alone and unattended, old King Priam of Troy goes to the tent of his enemy, Achilles, to ask for the corpse of his best-loved son, Prince Hector.

PRIAM: Great Achilles, you see, kneeling before you, a poor, heartbroken, lonely old king. I am Priam, King of Troy, your enemy. If it be your will to listen to my prayer, then let me stand and speak. If it be your will that I be murdered, here is my breast, ready for the sword of any who will do the deed.

ACHILLES: Stand, great Priam. Well know I what sorrow

lies in your heart, and what courage lies there, too. It shall not be for nothing that you have come unattended to the camp of the Greeks. Speak! What is your will?

PRIAM: I have come to ransom the body of my lately fallen son, Hector. It is not fitting that a royal prince should have no burial. In exchange, I bring you the finest gifts my kingdom has to offer: gold and armor, fine cloaks and rare wines.

ACHILLES: It shall be as you wish, King Priam. You may have the corpse of your son. You may take him home, and give him proper burial.

MUSIC: *Unhappy theme, in and under. Out.*

NARRATOR: Taking up the mutilated body of Hector, Priam makes his way back to the city of Troy, and once within its walls, calls out for all to come and pay homage to the dead hero.

PRIAM: Come, come, you men and women, babes and children of Troy! Come and see your dear, dead prince. Once you welcomed him home from battle with laughter and songs and happy voices. Welcome him now, in death, with tears and prayers and lamentations. Come, Queen Hecuba, look upon your son. Come, Andromache—give your dead husband your tears. Come, little Astyanax, and see your father's body. Come, come all of Troy, and see our prince . . . our hero . . . our hope . . . dead and ready for his grave.

MUSIC: *Unhappy theme, up and out.*

NARRATOR: As the fates have predicted, Achilles cannot live long after the death of Hector. Although he thinks himself invulnerable, a swift arrow from the bow of Paris finds Achilles' one weak spot, the heel of his foot, and the worthy Greek general falls in the field. In spite of this triumph, however, the Trojans cannot stem the tide of battle, and without the leadership of the now-dead Hector, all hope for Troy is gone. Within a short time, final victory goes to the Greeks. In his magnificent book, the *Aeneid*, Virgil tells the famous story of how the war came to its conclusion when the Greeks planned the strategic trickery of the great wooden horse. Regardless of the final victory, however, both Troy and Greece suffered deep losses, for the best men of both armies had sacrificed their lives. And so, after ten long, bitter years of strife and bloodshed, the Trojan War ended.

THE END

The Would-Be Gentleman

The Would-Be Gentleman

by Molière

Characters

MADAME JOURDAIN	LUCILE JOURDAIN
MONSIEUR JOURDAIN	CLEONTE
MUSIC MASTER	SALES CLERK
DANCING MASTER	NARRATOR
PHILOSOPHY TEACHER	

MADAME JOURDAIN: Monsieur Jourdain, my husband, you're a fool! Dressing up as though you're on your way to a fancy ball! Hiring language teachers, and dancing teachers, and fencing teachers, and music teachers! The next thing I know, you'll be paying somebody to teach you to breathe! And all because you think you can turn yourself into an aristocrat. Why don't you face the fact that you're a merchant, always have been a merchant, and always will be? You, a gentleman? Ha!

JOURDAIN: My dear wife, I don't see what the fuss is about, just because I respect quality. There is nothing to compare with genteel society. There's no true dignity except among the nobility. I would give my right arm to have been born a count or marquis. But since I wasn't born into the nobility, I'm going to buy my way in!

MUSIC: *Lighthearted theme, in and under. Out.*

NARRATOR: Did you just hear those two? They are Monsieur and Madame Jourdain, going at the same old argument between them for the—well, at least the twenty-seventh time this week! It's always the same old thing with them: *Monsieur* Jourdain wants to be a high-class nobleman, and *Madame* Jourdain wants simply to be Madame Jourdain! A great playwright once wrote a marvelously funny comedy about them, in which he told the entire story. Want to hear it? All right then: ladies and gentlemen, we now present the famous comedy by Molière, *The Would-Be Gentleman.*

MUSIC: *Gay theme, in, under, and out.*

NARRATOR: The play begins in a room in the house of Monsieur Jourdain in Paris. A simple merchant, Jourdain longs to be an aristocrat, a nobleman—a true gentleman of quality. And so he has hired all sorts of teachers and tailors, who, he hopes, will give him all of the knowledge and graces he needs. It's almost time for his daily lessons. Listen! Here come his music master and his dancing master, and I believe they're discussing this very student, Monsieur Jourdain!

MUSIC MASTER: I suppose Monsieur Jourdain will be along in a moment.

DANCING MASTER: Yes, he's generally right on time for his lessons.

MUSIC MASTER: We're both being kept pretty busy with him, eh, dancing master?

DANCING MASTER: Indeed we are!

MUSIC MASTER: Ah, this fellow Jourdain is just what we need, with his fantastic notions of gentility and gallantry. I only wish there were more people like him!

DANCING MASTER: I can't agree altogether. For his own sake I would like to see him have a little more understanding of the arts.

MUSIC MASTER: All the same, you don't refuse to take his money!

DANCING MASTER: Of course not! But it would be helpful if he had even a little taste!

MUSIC MASTER: Expecting taste from Monsieur Jourdain is like expecting cows to give wine instead of milk! I'm satisfied just to tell him a lot of nonsense that will keep him happy, and collect my fee.

DANCING MASTER: Hush! Here he comes!

JOURDAIN (*Fading on*): Ah, good morning, gentlemen. And what are we going to do today? Are you going to show me some more of your tricks?

DANCING MASTER: Tricks, Monsieur Jourdain? What tricks?

JOURDAIN: You know. Your dialogues or prologues or whatever it is—your singing and dancing!

MUSIC MASTER: Music and dancing are not tricks, sir!

JOURDAIN: Well, whatever it is, music master. Oh, I almost forgot. I want your opinions of my new suit! Isn't it handsome?

MUSIC MASTER: Oh, quite! (*Aside, in low voice*) Quite hideous, that is!

DANCING MASTER: It's just right! (*Aside, in low voice*) Just right for a fool!

JOURDAIN: Look at these colors, how elegantly they become me! You could search throughout Paris, and not another gentleman would you find that has a suit like this one!

DANCING MASTER: I well believe that!

JOURDAIN: My tailor tells me all the gentlemen of quality dress this way. Look here: seventy-five ribbons on each sleeve! And such exquisite taste, so simple and conservative. Do you realize that this suit is not the least bit gaudy? That's very rare! There are only five colors in it: pink, gold, cerise, yellow and chartreuse!

DANCING MASTER: A most elegant garment!

MUSIC MASTER: I only wish I had one like it!

JOURDAIN: Ah-ha, but you could not afford such a suit. I tell you I paid quite a fortune for it. Yes, yes, I always say, "Clothes make the man."

MUSIC MASTER: They certainly make *you!* (*Aside, in low voice*) They make an idiot of you!

JOURDAIN: But enough of clothes. What are you going to teach me today?

MUSIC MASTER: Ah, sir, today you will learn the notes of the scale.

JOURDAIN: I may not be a very good pupil, sir. The only notes I understand are those in the bank, and as for scales—only the kind that fish have.

MUSIC MASTER: But sir, you must study, study, study your music, and then you will understand.

JOURDAIN: Does the aristocracy study music?

MUSIC MASTER: But of course, monsieur.

DANCING MASTER: Almost as avidly as they study dancing!

JOURDAIN: Then I will study music and dancing as well! But I don't know where I'll find the time. I've already a fencing master, and a speech teacher, and now I've taken on a teacher of philosophy!

MUSIC MASTER: Well, there is something in philosophy, but music, sir, music—

DANCING MASTER: And dancing, music and dancing! What else does one need?

JOURDAIN: You have convinced me! If people of quality do it, so shall I!

MUSIC MASTER: Wonderful, monsieur! And now today's lesson is over, as the hour is up.

DANCING MASTER: If you will be so good as to pay us, monsieur, we shall be on our way.

JOURDAIN: Oh, certainly, certainly. Here is your money.

MUSIC MASTER: Thank you, sir. Oh, if only all my students were as quick to learn their music as you have been today!

DANCING MASTER: Never have I had a more apt ballet pupil than you!

JOURDAIN (*Pleased*): Really? How nice! Now you both be sure to come back tomorrow, and we shall have another lesson!

DANCING MASTER: Goodbye, Monsieur Jourdain.

MUSIC MASTER: Goodbye, Monsieur Jourdain.

JOURDAIN: Goodbye!

MUSIC: *Gay theme, in and under. Fades out.*

NARRATOR: As you can see, Monsieur Jourdain is certainly getting his money's worth from his tutors, for though he may not be learning much, they praise and flatter him so that he is glad to pay their fees. But here comes the philosophy teacher. Let's hear how *his* lesson goes!

JOURDAIN: Ah, good morning, philosophy teacher. What are *you* going to teach me?

PHILOSOPHY TEACHER: What would you like to learn?

JOURDAIN: Whatever I can, for I want above all things to become a scholar. I have never gotten over the fact that my parents didn't *force* me to be brilliant when I was young!

PHILOSOPHY TEACHER: Have you mastered the rudiments of the sciences?

JOURDAIN: Oh, yes! I can read—and write, too!

PHILOSOPHY TEACHER: Then shall I teach you logic?

JOURDAIN: Certainly! Yes! Indeed! Logic is just what I've *always* wanted to know. But one question.

PHILOSOPHY TEACHER: Yes?

JOURDAIN: What *is* logic?

PHILOSOPHY TEACHER: Logic instructs us in the three processes of reasoning.

JOURDAIN: And what are the three processes of reasoning?

PHILOSOPHY TEACHER: Why, the first process, the second process, and the third process, of course!

JOURDAIN: Oh, no, that sounds much too complicated! Teach me how to write beautiful letters; there's something I can use.

PHILOSOPHY TEACHER: Do you wish to write in verse?

JOURDAIN: No, no, none of your verse stuff for me!

PHILOSOPHY TEACHER: Then you wish to learn prose?

JOURDAIN: No, no, neither verse *nor* prose.

PHILOSOPHY TEACHER: But it must be in one or the other. Whatever isn't prose is verse, and whatever isn't verse is prose!

JOURDAIN: And talking, such as I am doing now: which is that?

PHILOSOPHY TEACHER: That is prose.

JOURDAIN: Do you mean to tell me that when I say to

my servant, "Get me my slippers," or I say to my wife, "You are an old nag!" that I am speaking prose?

PHILOSOPHY TEACHER: Certainly, sir!

JOURDAIN: Well, my goodness! Here I've been talking prose for forty years and never known it, and grateful I am that you've told me.

PHILOSOPHY TEACHER: You are a very quick student, Monsieur Jourdain. That's all for today's lesson. If you will now pay me my fee, I shall come again tomorrow.

JOURDAIN: Certainly. Here you are.

PHILOSOPHY TEACHER: Thank you, kind gentleman!

JOURDAIN: Eh? What did you call me?

PHILOSOPHY TEACHER: Kind gentleman.

JOURDAIN: Well, thank you! Just fancy, "kind gentleman!" Here's an extra gold piece for your "kind gentleman."

PHILOSOPHY TEACHER: I am indeed obliged, my lord.

JOURDAIN (*Happily*): "My lord!" Oh, my goodness! Here is another gold piece. Only fancy! "My lord"!

PHILOSOPHY TEACHER: Oh, you are too kind, your grace!

JOURDAIN: "Your grace! Your grace!" Take this for "your grace!"

PHILOSOPHY TEACHER: My lord, I thank your lordship for your grace's liberality!

JOURDAIN (*With a sigh of relief*): It's just as well he stopped at "your grace." I might have given him the whole purse!

MUSIC: *Sprightly theme, in and under. Fades out.*

NARRATOR: Now do not suppose that Monsieur Jourdain's wife approves of all her husband's carrying on. Quite the contrary! Whatever he does to appear more like a gentleman, she immediately finds fault with. Of his clothes, Madame Jourdain has this to say:

MME. JOURDAIN: What are you doing in that get-up? Tell me, husband: Are you planning on applying for a job as a circus clown?

NARRATOR: Of the dancing lessons she says this:

MME. JOURDAIN: Are you learning to dance for the time when you'll be too feeble to walk?

NARRATOR: And of the fencing lessons:

MME. JOURDAIN: Are you learning to fence because you want to murder somebody?

NARRATOR: But Madame Jourdain's biggest complaint to her husband is about the way he is treating their daughter, a lovely eighteen-year-old girl named Lucile.

MME. JOURDAIN: Why don't you give up all this foolishness and horseplay, my husband? You'd do much better to think about getting a husband for your daughter!

JOURDAIN: I'll think about getting Lucile married when a suitable husband comes along. Till that time, I intend to give my mind to studying and learning.

MME. JOURDAIN: No doubt all your knowledge is very useful!

JOURDAIN: Of course it is. For example, do you know what you are talking this very moment?

MME. JOURDAIN: Good common sense is what I'm talking!

JOURDAIN: That's not what I mean. What sort of speech are you using?

MME. JOURDAIN: Plain, understandable speech!

JOURDAIN: You're talking prose, that's what you're talking! You see what it is to be a scholar?

MME. JOURDAIN: A fine scholar you are! You can't even settle your daughter's wedding. She is in love with Cleonte. He is in love with her. But will you let them marry? Oh no, not you! You even forbid the poor girl to *see* her beloved. You call yourself a scholar? You call yourself a father? Well, *I* call you a *fool!*

MUSIC: *Sprightly theme, in, under, and out.*

NARRATOR: Did you ever hear the like of it? Springtime, and in Paris, and this Monsieur Jourdain refuses to allow his daughter to see her beloved. Such injustice! Such cruelty! However, there are ways of getting around such things, and very often, though Papa says "No," Mama will say "Yes." And in many households, it is Mama who has her way. So, this very afternoon, Madame Jourdain allows the handsome young man who loves Lucile to call. His name is Cleonte, and when he arrives, the lovely young girl greets him joyfully!

LUCILE (*A sweet girl, overjoyed*): Cleonte! Is it really you? Mama told me we would have company today, but I never dreamed . . . !

CLEONTE: Ah, my sweet Lucile. That is your trouble! Dearest love, you *should* have dreamed!

LUCILE: From now on, my beloved Cleonte, I shall always dream—and only of you!

MME. JOURDAIN (*Fading on*): Cleonte, my boy, how glad I am that you have come. And just at the right moment, too. My husband is coming in, so take your chances and ask him to let you marry Lucile.

CLEONTE: Ah, madame, no command could be nearer to my desires, or more gracious, or more acceptable to me.

JOURDAIN (*Fading on*): Now, wife, who is this company you want me to meet? (*Angrily*) What? Is it you, Cleonte?

CLEONTE: Sir, I have come to put to you a request that I have long been considering. May I ask the privilege and honor of becoming your son-in-law?

JOURDAIN: Before giving you a reply, sir, I must ask you one question. Are you a gentleman?

CLEONTE: I was born, sir, of honorable parents. I have served six years with our glorious French army, and have, I believe, the money to maintain a pretty fair place in the world. But if you mean to ask me if I am one of the nobility, I must, in all honesty, tell you that I am not, as you put it, a gentleman.

JOURDAIN: That settles it then. My daughter is not for you!

CLEONTE: What?

LUCILE: But, Papa!

JOURDAIN: If you aren't a gentleman, you can't have my daughter.

MME. JOURDAIN: What are you talking about? You and your gentlemen! Are we descended from St. Louis? Was Marie Antoinette your cousin? If so, I never knew it before! We are plain, decent, honest people—and so is Cleonte!

JOURDAIN: I know what I'm talking about. Our daughter will marry a gentleman! It is my business to see that she rises in the world, and I mean to make her a marchioness!

LUCILE: A marchioness!

MME. JOURDAIN: Heaven forbid! Why should she marry above her station? Do you want her children to be ashamed to call you "grandpa?" Do you want her husband to refuse to sit down at our table with us?

JOURDAIN: My mind is made up that she shall be a marchioness, and if you provoke me further, I'll—I'll make her a duchess!

MUSIC: *Gay theme, in, under, and out.*

NARRATOR: Needless to say, Madame Jourdain is furious, Cleonte is disappointed, and as for Lucile—she is heart-broken. But there is a saying: "When the heart says 'Yes,' nobody dares say 'No.' " And so the three put their heads together to try to think of a way out of the situation.

MME. JOURDAIN: Don't lose heart yet, Cleonte. Lucile, my dear, look more cheerful. It is not the end of the world.

LUCILE: It might as well be!

MME. JOURDAIN: Nothing of the sort. We'll get around that foolish father of yours yet. First of all, you must tell him firmly that if you can't marry Cleonte, you will marry nobody at all.

CLEONTE: And then . . . ?

MME. JOURDAIN: And then . . . well, we'll just have to wait and see.

MUSIC: *Lighthearted theme, in, under, and out.*

NARRATOR: During the days that follow, Monsieur Jourdain becomes more and more active in his pursuit of learning.

MUSIC MASTER: Now then, sir, sing the scale!

JOURDAIN (*In a hoarse voice, off-key*): Do-re-mi-fa-sol . . .

PHILOSOPHY TEACHER: Come, Monsieur Jourdain. What is natural science?

JOURDAIN: Natural science explains the—principles of natural—phenomena in the poppycock—populace—*properties* of matter!

DANCING MASTER: Come, Monsieur Jourdain. Faster! Dance faster! One and two and three and *leap!*

JOURDAIN (*Puffing heavily*): One—and two—and three—and—

SOUND: *Crash of glass.*

NARRATOR: And while Monsieur Jourdain is studying and learning and growing wiser and wiser, the others continue to try to find a way to thwart his marriage plans for Lucile.

MME. JOURDAIN: How about this? We could—no, that wouldn't work.

LUCILE: Maybe if we—no, it would never do.

CLEONTE: Wouldn't it be possible for us to—no, that's no use.

MME. JOURDAIN: How about—

LUCILE: What if we—

MME. JOURDAIN: Couldn't we—

LUCILE: Shouldn't we—

CLEONTE: Wait! I have it! Just the idea! And it's so simple, I don't understand why we didn't think of it before.

LUCILE: What is it?

MME. JOURDAIN: Tell us!

CLEONTE: Wait and see. Just leave everything to me!

MUSIC: *Happy theme, in, under, and out.*

NARRATOR: So Cleonte has hit upon an idea. What do you suppose it could be? He wouldn't try physical violence —he's too kind-hearted. Surely he wouldn't be planning an elopement—he's too honorable! What's this? Cleonte is going into a shop. The sign on the door says "Theatrical Costumes for Rent and Sale." What can he be up to?

SALES CLERK: Yes, monsieur? What can I do for you?

CLEONTE: I'm looking for a disguise.

SALES CLERK: Yes, sir. But what kind? Is it for a show? Or for a party?

CLEONTE: No, it's—it's for a wedding.

SALES CLERK: A wedding! A disguise for a wedding, did you say?

CLEONTE: That's right. I'd like something Oriental—such as a royal prince might wear.

SALES CLERK (*Humoring him, as though afraid* CLEONTE *were mad*): Of course. A Grand Turk's costume—as a disguise—for a wedding.

CLEONTE: One with a beard!

SALES CLERK: With a beard. You're going to play a practical joke on the groom, are you?

CLEONTE: Quite the contrary. I *am* the groom!

MUSIC: *Happy theme, in and under. Out.*

NARRATOR: So that's it! Cleonte is going to dress up in the foreign costume, put on the false beard, and present himself to Monsieur Jourdain. Why, there he is now, all decked out in his scarlet turban, green bodice, purple pantaloons and bushy black beard. In that costume, Cleonte could fool even his own mother! Why, if I didn't know better, I'd say it was the Grand Turk himself! Oh, clever Cleonte! I wonder if his scheme will save the day.

CLEONTE (*In solemn tones*): The blessings of Allah upon you, Monsieur Jourdain.

JOURDAIN (*Surprised*): What? What? Who are you, strange man, that call me by my name?

CLEONTE: I am the Paladin, the son of the Grand Turk.

JOURDAIN (*Amazed*): The son of the—of the Grand Turk himself?

CLEONTE: Indeed, I am his oldest and best-loved son.

JOURDAIN: Really? Oh, your honor—your grace—your highness! What is it that you want? What can I do for you?

CLEONTE: You can save my life, Monsieur Jourdain—and I know you will not hesitate to do it, for I understand that you are a true gentleman.

JOURDAIN (*Amazed*): I? A gentleman? (*Collecting himself*) Oh, of course! I! A gentleman! Yes, yes, a gentleman, I!

CLEONTE: And because you are a gentleman, I know you will not hesitate to save my life.

JOURDAIN: Your life? Gladly, your lordship. But how am I, of all people, able to do that?

CLEONTE: You see, Monsieur Jourdain, I have fallen in love with your daughter, Lucile.

JOURDAIN (*Amazed*): With Lucile?

CLEONTE: Yes, with Lucile. And if you will not consent to my marrying her, I know I shall die of a broken heart.

JOURDAIN: Die! Oh, no, you mustn't do that! We mustn't let that happen!

CLEONTE: Then you will consent to her becoming my wife?

JOURDAIN: Consent? Why, I should say so! Consent! And you, the son of the Grand Turk himself, the wealthiest potentate of the East! Yes, yes, my boy—I mean, your highness. And to think I would have settled for making her a marchioness. Now she's to be a princess! I can hardly believe it! A miracle! That's what it is, a miracle! (*Calling out*) Wife! Daughter! Come at once! (*To* CLEONTE) Sir, I wish you the strength of serpents and the wisdom of lions! Son of the Grand Turk!

MME. JOURDAIN (*Fading on*): What is it, husband?

LUCILE (*Fading on*): Yes, Father, what is it?

JOURDAIN (*Joyfully*): Come here, my girl. Give your hand

to this gentleman, who has done you the honor of asking to marry you.

LUCILE (*Aghast*): What? Me? Marry this—this—him, Father?

JOURDAIN: Yes, yes. Marry him, and thank Heaven—that is, thank Allah—for your good fortune!

LUCILE (*Firmly*): But I've told you, Father, I will marry only Cleonte!

CLEONTE: Allow me to talk to her a moment, monsieur. I'm sure I can convince her to marry me!

JOURDAIN (*Fading slightly*): Certainly! Certainly!

CLEONTE (*In close, whispering*): Look, Lucile! It's I, Cleonte! This disguise is only to trick your father!

LUCILE (*Happily, in a whisper*): Oh, my darling. How clever of you! (*Aloud*) Very well, Father. I see it is my duty to marry whom you choose for me. You shall make the decision!

JOURDAIN: What decision is there to be made? He's a gentleman!

MME. JOURDAIN (*With loud determination*): Perhaps Lucile does not object to this foolishness, but I do! Have you gone mad?

JOURDAIN: Not at all. I intend to marry my daughter to the son of the Grand Turk!

MME. JOURDAIN: He looks more like a turkey than a Turk!

LUCILE: Mother, dear . . .

MME. JOURDAIN: You be quiet, you hussy, you. And after swearing to be true to Cleonte! Do you call this faithfulness?

CLEONTE: Madame, grant me one word in private, and I promise you will accept my marriage to your daughter.

MME. JOURDAIN: That, I assure you, I will never do. You

may tell me what you have to say. But don't think for a moment I'll change my mind.

CLEONTE (*Softly*): Good Madame Jourdain, I've been trying to let you know that I'm just playing up to your husband's fantastic ideas!

MME. JOURDAIN (*In a whisper*): What's this? What's this?

CLEONTE: I, the son of the Grand Turk, am none other than Cleonte!

MME. JOURDAIN: Oh, so that's it! (*Aloud*) Well, husband, this gentleman has explained everything to my satisfaction! I give my consent.

JOURDAIN: I knew you'd see reason at last! When shall the wedding be?

MME. JOURDAIN: Immediately!

LUCILE: Now!

CLEONTE: At once!

JOURDAIN: Excellent! Send for the notary! Send for the priest!

MME. JOURDAIN: Ah, husband, this is a wedding you'll never forget!

JOURDAIN: Of course not! It isn't everyone who can become the father-in-law of a prince, or have a daughter that's a princess! And to think of that *bourgeois* Cleonte having the nerve to ask for her hand in marriage! Tell me, my wife. Was there ever a bigger fool than that Cleonte?

MME. JOURDAIN (*Shrewdly*): Yes, my husband, I think there was—*one*.

JOURDAIN: And who was that?

MME. JOURDAIN: Ah, my gentleman of a husband, my nobleman of a husband, my shrewd, bright, shining aristocrat of a husband, that is a story that I shall tell you in detail *after* the wedding.

JOURDAIN (*Laughing*): Very well, wife. After the wedding!
  There's nothing I like better than the story of a fool!
  Ha, ha, ha! I hope it's a good story! (*Grandly*) It must
  be a story that's fit to be told to the *gentleman Jourdain!*
  (*All join in laughter.*)
MUSIC: *Wedding march, full to finish.*

THE END

The Lady or the Tiger?

The Lady or the Tiger?

by Frank R. Stockton

Characters

SIPTAH, *the High Priest*	GUARD
KING KHAF-RA	TUOSHRI, *the jailer*
CHARMIAN, *the princess*	THREE PEASANTS
TAIA, *her serving-woman*	NARRATOR
ANAKRON, *the king's slave*	

NARRATOR: Long ago there lived a semi-barbaric king whose chief aim in life was to be just. To be a good king interested him very little, for semi-barbarians know practically nothing of goodness. To be a strong king interested him even less, for his father before him had been so ruthless an enemy to all the surrounding kingdoms that they had long since been destroyed. But to be a *just* king interested the semi-barbaric monarch enormously, for he realized that justice is always relative. When a crime is committed, one can be truly just, only if one knows all the facts. Every element that is involved in the act—no matter how small or obscure—has to be understood. And this, thought the king, is impossible. He pondered the matter of justice; he philosophized about justice; he considered it, riddled it, mused upon it . . .

179

but to no avail. He could not be sure that he was a truly just king. And so, at last, he consulted his High Priest about it.

SOUND: *Oriental gong.*

SIPTAH (*Fading on*): O noble King Khaf-Ra, emperor of all the lands on which the sun rises in the morning, ruler of all the territories on which the moon smiles at night, what is your bidding?

KING: Ah, Siptah, my faithful High Priest. I am glad you have come, for I have great need of your counsel.

SIPTAH: Is it to foretell the future, Your Majesty? To read the stars?

KING: I am no simpleton, Siptah. I know as well as you that no man can read the future, nor tell what hidden mysteries lie behind the stars.

SIPTAH: Is it to soothe your mind, then, Your Majesty? You are troubled by dreams?

KING: Not by dreams, Siptah. I am troubled by thoughts.

SIPTAH: By thoughts? I do not understand.

KING: I have been thinking of justice. Day and night, it seems, my mind cannot escape from thinking on it, musing upon it, puzzling it out. Tell me, Siptah: what is justice?

SIPTAH (*Vaguely*): Ah, Your Majesty, justice is the divine gift of the gods.

KING (*Impatiently*): Don't tell me such foolish things, priest. I ask a straightforward question, and you must give me a straightforward answer.

SIPTAH (*Smoothly*): Justice, O king, is the first virtue. Justice sees by its own light, and drinks of its own balm.

KING (*Angrily*): Don't go on with this drivel! Why do you not tell me straight out what justice is? Why do you waste my time with this mumbo-jumbo? You anger me, my friend. If you do not satisfy me with an answer, I will pitch you to the tigers in the arena.

SIPTAH (*Slyly*): And will that be justice, Your Majesty?

KING (*Tiredly*): I don't know. No, it will not be justice. You have not answered my question because you cannot answer it. I know that it is not just to punish a man for that.

SIPTAH: There is your answer, sir. Justice can be determined only in an individual case. It does not exist as an isolated thing.

KING (*Grimly*): If, indeed, it exists at all. It's all so arbitrary, so open to error.

SIPTAH: But, Your Majesty, the king can never be in error.

KING: Oh, but I can, I can. I feel it in my heart. Whenever a man is brought before me on trial for his life, I pray to the gods that they give me the wisdom to be just. Whenever a man is found guilty of a crime, whenever a criminal is thrown to the tigers in the arena—I sit and watch. I listen to his screams, and I watch him die. And all the time my conscience keeps whispering to me: "Has justice been done in this case? Is it right that the man should be punished? Are you sure that it is meet he should die?"

SIPTAH: And *are* you sure?

KING: No, Siptah, I am not. And I have decided we must have a new way.

SIPTAH: A new way, sire?

KING: Yes. From now on, when a man is accused of a crime, he shall be his own judge, his own jury, and—perhaps —his own executioner. If we can never be sure of administering justice, we should not try to do it at all.

From this day forward, we will place the matter in the laps of the gods. *They* will decide the case—and their earthly agent will be the accused man himself. Listen, Siptah, I have a plan. *(Fading)* From now on, when a man has been accused of a crime in our kingdom . . .

MUSIC: *Dramatic theme, up full and out.*

NARRATOR: And so King Khaf-Ra began to explain to the High Priest, Siptah, his unique plan for administering justice. Siptah agreed that it was a wise and good plan. And the next day, seven blasts were blown on the royal ram's horn to summon the people to the steps of the temple, so that Siptah could announce the new method of dealing with criminals.

SOUND: *Long blast of a ram's horn, over murmur of a large crowd.*

SIPTAH *(Announcing in declamatory tones)*: Hear ye, hear ye, all ye lowly subjects of the noble King Khaf-Ra. By his royal command, all courts of law shall be abolished, all instruments of torture shall be destroyed, and all judges shall be relieved of their posts. From this day, the ninth in the month of Seleucus, in the year of the noble Cat Goddess Shorshi, all who are accused of criminal acts will be brought to the public arena. There they will be confronted with two doors. Behind one door will be a tiger, its claws sharpened on the bark of the eucalyptus tree, its hunger increased by four days of starvation. Behind the second door will stand a beautiful woman, suited in age and rank to the accused in question. At a sign from the King, the accused will choose a door, go to it, and open it. If he chooses the door behind which stands the tiger, he chooses death.

If he chooses the door behind which stands the lady, he will be married to her immediately, given a pension, and allowed to live a free and happy life. It will be the criminal's own choice, and only the will of the gods shall guide his hand. By order of the King. Hear ye, hear ye!

MUSIC: *Oriental theme, in and under. Out.*

NARRATOR: And so the original and novel plan of King Khaf-Ra, the semi-barbaric monarch who wished above all things to be just, became the new law of the land. The people were at first amazed, but the more they thought about the plan, the more it appealed to them.

1ST PEASANT: After all, it'll be a marvelous free show for the rest of us!

2ND PEASANT: Now the gods alone will decide who is guilty and who is innocent.

3RD PEASANT: And with some of the women in this kingdom—my wife, for example—choosing the tiger might not be so bad after all!

NARRATOR: Among those who heard Siptah announce the new decree was Charmian, princess of all the land, and beloved daughter of the King himself. That evening, as she sat at table with him, King Khaf-Ra questioned her about the new law.

KING: And did you hear the proclamation made by the High Priest Siptah, my lovely daughter?

CHARMIAN (*A girl of spirit, about eighteen*): Yes, Father, and I do wonder at it. To give up your power of life and death over your subjects—do you think it wise?

KING: It may not be wise, Charmian, my dear, but it is at least sensible. Why should *I* decide who is to live and who is to die? It is not for me to make such decisions. We have too many doubts, too many questions for that sort of game.

CHARMIAN: I do not think that I should have any doubts. I would know which man should die, which man should be spared.

KING: You, Charmian? Ah, no, the ways of justice confuse kings and wise men, my daughter. You're but a child, and would be even more confused.

CHARMIAN: I'm not a child any longer, Father. I'm a woman.

KING (*Kindly*): Of course you are, my darling. As a matter of fact, I want to talk with you on the subject of your growing up.

CHARMIAN: Yes, Father?

KING: The time will soon be at hand, my daughter, when we must think of finding you a husband.

CHARMIAN (*Alarmed*): A husband? Oh, no—no.

SOUND: *A glass breaking.*

CHARMIAN (*Gasping*): Oh, my wine!

KING: Why, you've dropped your glass, Charmian.

CHARMIAN: How clumsy of me! And wine spilling all over my dress! Taia, come here!

TAIA (*A young woman, fading on*): Yes, Your Highness?

CHARMIAN: Help me to clean my dress. I've spilled my wine.

TAIA: Yes, Your Highness.

KING: While your serving-woman cleans your dress, I'll call for my cupbearer, Anakron.

SOUND: *Clapping of hands three times.*

CHARMIAN (*Flustered*): Anakron? Why do you send for Anakron?

KING (*Surprised*): To bring you a fresh goblet of wine, daughter. Why else?

ANAKRON (*A young man, fading on*): Your Majesty, what is your will?

KING: Ah, Anakron. Give the Princess a fresh goblet, and fill it with wine.

ANAKRON: Certainly, Your Majesty.

CHARMIAN (*Confused*): No, Anakron, I don't want any— enough, enough, Taia, you're making the spot worse than ever. I'll clean the dress myself. Begone!

TAIA (*Fading*): Very well, Your Highness.

KING (*Confused*): Why are you so upset, my daughter? The poor serving-woman was doing her best.

CHARMIAN (*Trying to calm herself*): Yes, of course, Father. I—I don't know what is wrong with me. I shall apologize to her later.

KING (*Kindly*): Anakron, give the princess some wine. It will quiet her nerves.

ANAKRON (*In a low voice*): Will Her Highness have sweet wine, or dry?

CHARMIAN: Sweet—dry.

ANAKRON: Your hands are shaking, princess. Allow me to steady your glass. There, that's better.

CHARMIAN: I—I thank you, Anakron.

KING: Are you calmer now, my daughter?

CHARMIAN: Yes, Father. It—it was your talk of a husband that upset me. I—I didn't expect that.

KING (*Jovially*): But Anakron's wine has made you feel better, eh?

CHARMIAN: Yes, he—yes, Father, I feel better now.

KING (*Expansively*): I know. Anakron's wine always makes

me feel better when I get a bit jittery. You know, Anakron, you're the favorite of all my slaves.

ANAKRON (*Humbly*): You do me too much honor, sire.

KING (*Sighing contentedly*): It's a happy man who is king of a great land, has a beautiful daughter by his side, and a loyal slave to give him comfort. I'm a lucky man indeed.

NARRATOR: King Khaf-Ra, however, would not have been quite so contented had he known that his beautiful daughter and his loyal slave were more to each other than princess and servant. For the truth of the matter was— and this is why Her Highness had been so upset at the talk of choosing a husband—Princess Charmian and the slave Anakron were in love. Late that night, Princess Charmian paced the palace gardens, accompanied in the darkness only by her faithful serving-woman, Taia.

CHARMIAN (*Impatiently*): Why doesn't he come?

TAIA: Anakron will be here, your Highness. But it takes time. It is not easy for a slave to slip away unnoticed; there are guards everywhere.

CHARMIAN (*Anxiously*): Perhaps the guards have stopped him! Perhaps we are found out!

TAIA: Never fear, Your Highness. Anakron is brave—and strong. For such a man, even the impossible is easy. You must be patient.

CHARMIAN: It is easy for you to say "Be patient." You don't know what it is to be in love.

TAIA (*Simply*): That is not true, Your Highness.

CHARMIAN (*Delighted*): You are in love, my little one? With whom?

TAIA (*Evasively*): I cannot say, Your Highness. After all,

I am only a slave. I have no right to love. Besides, the one
I love belongs to another.

CHARMIAN (*Sadly*): Then your love is as hopeless as mine.

TAIA: Do not say "hopeless," Your Highness. Perhaps His
Majesty would forgive you, and allow you to marry
Anakron.

CHARMIAN: Never. I am a princess, and he is a slave. It cannot be. (*In anguish*) Oh, why doesn't he come?

TAIA (*Eagerly*): Your Highness, I heard a footstep!

CHARMIAN: Where?

TAIA: By the wall.

CHARMIAN: Yes! I saw—

TAIA: A shadow!

CHARMIAN: It is he! Leave us, Taia. But keep watch, and
if anyone comes, run at once and tell us.

TAIA (*Fading*): I will keep watch, Your Highness.

ANAKRON (*Fading on*): Charmian, my princess! Oh, my
love.

CHARMIAN: Anakron! How long I have waited for you. I
began to think you would never come.

ANAKRON: The King sits with his council. It was not easy
for me to slip away.

CHARMIAN: It is almost dawn.

ANAKRON: We must make the most of each minute we have.
Oh, if only we did not have to meet like this—in shad-
ows, hiding from everyone.

CHARMIAN: I know. But it cannot be helped, my love. You
know the penalty if we are found together.

ANAKRON (*Firmly*): Sometimes I wish they *would* find us.
I think I would not mind death, if once I could tell the
world I love you.

CHARMIAN: Oh, do not say such things, my love. I could not bear to go on living without you. I know it is hard this way, but . . .

TAIA (*Fading on, in breathless haste*): Your Highness, they are coming!

CHARMIAN: Coming? Who?

TAIA: The king's guards! It is the king himself who leads them.

CHARMIAN: Anakron, you must hide!

TAIA: But where?

ANAKRON: It is too late!

SOUND: *Footsteps of several men, running, coming closer.*

CHARMIAN: You must try! Save yourself, Anakron!

TAIA: There is yet time, Anakron! Fly!

GUARD (*Off mike, calling out*): Stop, in the name of the great King Khaf-Ra.

CHARMIAN (*Woefully*): It is too late!

KING (*Fading on*): Charmian, my daughter . . .

CHARMIAN: Father!

KING: What is the meaning of this?

CHARMIAN: Father, I can explain . . .

KING (*Coldly*): There is nothing to be explained. I see at once all there is to see. Guards, seize that man.

GUARD: Yes, Your Majesty.

CHARMIAN: Father, have pity!

KING: Charmian, my child, how sorry I am I cannot say. But this man is a slave and had no right to come near you. You know the penalty.

GUARD (*Slightly off mike*): He is securely bound, Your Majesty.

KING (*Sadly*): Oh, Anakron, Anakron, favorite of all my slaves—that you should be the source of so much grief.

ANAKRON: I am sad, too, Your Majesty—not that I must die, but that I am so far beneath the station of my love.

TAIA (*Earnestly*): Sire, if a slave may be heard, have pity on him.

KING: You, too, Taia? No, it cannot be. You have all heard the decree made by my High Priest, Siptah. Guards, take the slave to the prisons at the public arena.

CHARMIAN: No, Father, no.

KING: It must be. Anakron will be the first to choose: the lady or the tiger.

MUSIC: *Dramatic theme, up and out.*

NARRATOR: So the cupbearer to the king, Anakron the slave, was borne away, bound securely hand and foot, to lie in the prison of the public arena, awaiting the day when his fate should be decided by a trick of luck, the choice of the gods, or the guidance of the evil spirit. What he felt at the approaching event, it would be hard to say. What the princess felt, however, was altogether clear.

CHARMIAN (*Weeping*): Oh, Taia, Taia, how can I bear it?

TAIA: You must be calm and controlled, Your Highness, as befits a princess. Yours is not the first love to end in death.

CHARMIAN: How calmly you say it. How glib you are. But *my* heart is breaking!

TAIA (*Simply*): Mine, too, Your Highness.

CHARMIAN (*Taken aback*): What's this? What's this?

TAIA (*Calmly*): Yes, Your Highness, my heart breaks, too, for Anakron is the man I love.

CHARMIAN (*Shrieking*): Traitor! You loved him—even as I?

TAIA: Such things cannot be helped.

CHARMIAN (*Weeping*): Oh, where are the gods at such a time? Is there no comfort for me now?

MUSIC: *Unhappy theme, in and under.*

NARRATOR: But if the gods heard her cries, they did not respond. Princess Charmian was inconsolable. At last she made up her mind to humble herself before her father, in a last attempt to change his mind about the awful punishment that awaited Anakron.

CHARMIAN: Father, can you deny the tears, the prayers, the cries of your only child?

KING (*Sternly*): It breaks my heart to see you so, Charmian, but what is to be cannot be changed. You know I have always tried to be just. But there can be no justice if there are two sets of laws . . . one for kings and one for slaves. All must be treated the same. Anakron must enter the arena.

CHARMIAN (*Bitterly*): It was Taia, my serving-woman, wasn't it, who carried the tale to your ear. Yes, of course; she loves Anakron herself. What torture it must have been for her to see him in my arms. And rather than let him be happy with another, she played traitor to us both and reported what she knew to you. I'll have her whipped! I'll sell her to the hardest slave master I can find. Taia shall rue the day she dared to betray a princess.

KING: Gently, my daughter, gently. You were betrayed by your own hand. Do you think I have not eyes in my head? That day you dropped your goblet at table—do you think I did not see what passed between your eyes and Anakron's as he refilled your glass? Your blushes—your stammering—your reluctance to talk of taking a husband. They were the spies that betrayed you, not your servant Taia. She never breathed a word.

CHARMIAN: I know she did. She loves him, too; she told me so herself! And now Anakron must die.

KING: Perhaps, my daughter, he will not die.

CHARMIAN (*Hopefully*): You will spare him, then?

KING: He must enter the arena. But perhaps he will choose the door behind which stands a lady, waiting to become his bride. Do not forget that only one door hides a tiger; behind the other will stand a woman befitting the prisoner's rank and station.

CHARMIAN: There is no woman in this kingdom fit for Anakron save myself.

KING: Yes, daughter, there is one.

CHARMIAN: And that is—?

KING: Your serving-woman, Taia.

MUSIC: *Dramatic theme, in and under.*

NARRATOR: And so it was decided. Anakron would enter the arena to make his choice within three days. The news was published far and wide, and all the citizens made plans to attend the great ordeal. On every hand, people were wondering the same thing: which would he choose, the door which hid the ferocious beast, or the door which hid Taia, the lovely slave girl who loved him. And all were content to wait three days to see how the trial would end . . . all but one. Princess Charmian alone could not wait, could not rest. All she could think about was finding a way to save her beloved Anakron. Late one night, she slipped out of the palace, and made her way to the arena, where, in a dungeon far below the earth, the unhappy slave awaited his doom.

SOUND: *Creaking of a jail door.*

TUOSHRI (*A gruff old man*): Wait. Who goes there?

CHARMIAN: It is I, Princess Charmian.

TUOSHRI (*In awe*): Your Highness! Why have you come here to the prisons? This is no place for a woman, let alone a princess.

CHARMIAN: Who dares to give advice to me?

TUOSHRI (*Meekly*): I am Tuoshri, the jailer.

CHARMIAN: Listen to me, Tuoshri. I must see the slave Anakron—in private.

TUOSHRI: But . . . but, Your Highness, it is against the law.

CHARMIAN: I am the Princess Charmian, and above the law. I order you to admit me. Here is a bag of silver for your trouble.

TUOSHRI: I—I cannot refuse you, Princess. But I beg you, if anyone finds you here, do not say that it was Tuoshri who let you in.

CHARMIAN (*Coldly*): I shall say nothing. See that you do likewise.

TUOSHRI (*Fading*): Yes, Your Highness. Come this way . . .

SOUND: *Clanking of a jail door opening.*

MUSIC: *Eerie theme, in and under.*

NARRATOR: With the old jailer guiding her, Princess Charmian descended to the dungeons.

CHARMIAN (*Whispering*): Anakron! Anakron! Can you hear me?

SOUND: *Clanking of chains.*

ANAKRON: Who's there?

CHARMIAN: It is I, Charmian, my love.

ANAKRON (*Surprised*): Charmian! What are you doing in this place?

CHARMIAN: I come to bring you good news.

ANAKRON: Has the king relented, then?

CHARMIAN: Alas, no. His mind is firm.

ANAKRON: What then?

CHARMIAN: Tomorrow, when the sun is at its highest in the sky, they will bring you to the arena to make your choice.

ANAKRON: What choice? Either will be hideous to me. Without you, do you think I care if I live or die?

CHARMIAN: There's nothing to be done. You must choose, Anakron: the lady or the tiger.

ANAKRON: What is the news you say you bring?

CHARMIAN: Just this. I promise you that somehow I will find out which door hides the beast and which the woman.

ANAKRON: But that is impossible. Only the High Priest, Siptah will know that.

CHARMIAN: Never mind about that. I swear to you I will find out his secret.

ANAKRON: But how will you let me know?

CHARMIAN: When they lead you into the arena, you must look until you find me. I will be sitting in the royal box beside my father. Pay no attention to the screams of the populace or to the sun that will be shining in its heat. Do not listen to the sound of the trumpets, or even to the sound of your own heart. Only lift your eyes to mine, and I will give you a sign.

ANAKRON: You are sure that you will find out the secret?

CHARMIAN: I swear I will find it out. Until tomorrow, then, Anakron, goodbye.

ANAKRON: Goodbye, my love . . . until tomorrow.

NARRATOR: That night, as all the kingdom lay asleep, Princess Charmian went to the temple of the Cat Goddess Shorshi to see the High Priest, Siptah. What words she used, no one will ever know. But after several hours, Princess Charmian emerged from the inner court, stood on the steps of the great temple, gazed up at the silver-white moon, and whispered aloud to the sky:

CHARMIAN: The secret is mine! I know which door! I know which door!

MUSIC: *Active theme, up and out.*

NARRATOR: The next day, all the populace gathered in the great arena. At the precise moment when the sun reached its zenith, a fanfare of trumpets was heard.

SOUND: *Fanfare of trumpets, followed by roaring of crowd, up, then under and out.*

NARRATOR: At the far end of the arena, a door was thrown open, and Anakron walked into the blazing sunlight. The crowd roared, and all eyes shifted from the slave to the two wooden doors at the other side of the arena. Which would he choose? Dazed by the light, after so many nights in the darkness of the dungeon, Anakron had only one thought in mind. Quickly he searched the arena until he saw the royal box, decked in rugs of fur, with pennons flying. Steadfastly he moved toward the box, until his eyes met those of the Princess Charmian.

CHARMIAN (*In a whisper*): Anakron!

NARRATOR: And in return, his quick and anxious glance asked a single question.

ANAKRON (*On filter mike, if possible*): Which door, my love? Which door?

NARRATOR: The princess' right arm lay on the cushioned

parapet before her. She raised her hand, and made a slight, quick movement toward the right. No one but her love saw her. Every eye was fixed on the man in the arena. He turned, and with a firm and rapid step he walked across the empty space. Every heart stopped beating, as without the slightest hesitation he went to the door on the right, and opened it.

SOUND: *Long, shrill blast of the ram's horn.*

NARRATOR (*In a more quiet conversational tone*): Now, the point of the story is this: did the tiger come out of that door, or did the lady? Did the Princess Charmian love the slave Anakron so much that she would rather see him live in the arms of the beautiful slave girl, Taia, who also loved him, than to have him meet a cruel death? Or did Charmian's passion arouse such jealousy in her that she would rather see Anakron die than live as Taia's husband? Would it not be better for him to die, and go to wait for her in the blessed regions of eternity? And yet, that awful tiger! She had imagined it so vividly. Those shrieks, that blood! Which came out of the door: the lady or the tiger? (*Pause*) Which did the Princess Charmian choose? (*Pause*) Which would *you* have chosen?

MUSIC: *Dramatic chords, full to finish.*

THE END

Tom Sawyer and Injun Joe

Tom Sawyer and Injun Joe

from *The Adventures of Tom Sawyer* by Mark Twain

Characters

HUCKLEBERRY FINN	TWO WOMEN
TOM SAWYER	TWO MEN
DR. ROBINSON	THE JUDGE
MUFF POTTER	PROSECUTING ATTORNEY
INJUN JOE	DEFENSE ATTORNEY
AUNT POLLY	TOWNSPEOPLE

HUCKLEBERRY (*Calling out*): Hey, Tom! You, Tom! Wait up a second, can't you? Hey, Tom! Tom Sawyer!

MUSIC: *Delightful theme, up and out.*

HUCKLEBERRY: Golly, Tom. I thought I'd never catch up with you.

TOM: Hello, Huckleberry.

HUCKLEBERRY: Hello yourself, and see how you like it.

TOM: Hey, what's that you have?

HUCKLEBERRY: Dead cat.

TOM: Let me see him, Huck. My, he's pretty stiff. Where'd you get him?

HUCKLEBERRY: Bought him off a boy. I gave him a blue ticket and a bladder that I got at the slaughterhouse.

TOM: Say, what are dead cats good for, Huck?

HUCKLEBERRY: Good for? Why, to cure warts with!

TOM: No! Is that so? I know something that's better: spunk water!

HUCKLEBERRY: Spunk water! That's no good. Why, Bob Tanner tried it, and it didn't work. And he told Jeff Thatcher, and Jeff told Johnny Baker, and Johnny told Jim Hollis, and Jim told Ben Rogers, and Ben told Siddy, and Siddy told me. There now!

TOM: What of it? They'll all lie! But, say, how do you cure 'em with dead cats?

HUCKLEBERRY: Why, you take your cat and go to the graveyard, along about midnight, when somebody that was wicked has been buried. When it's midnight, a devil will come, or maybe two or three. But you can't see 'em, you can only hear em—something like the wind—or maybe hear 'em talk. When they're taking that fellow away, you heave your cat after 'em and say, "Devil follow corpse, cat follow devil, warts follow cat, I'm done with ye!" That'll fetch *any* wart.

TOM: Sounds right. Did you ever try it, Hucky?

HUCKLEBERRY: No, but old Mother Hopkins told me.

TOM: I reckon it's so then, because they say she's a witch.

HUCKLEBERRY: Say she is! Why, Tom Sawyer, I *know* she is. She witched my pap. Pap says so his own self.

TOM: Why, that's awful. How'd he know she was witching him?

HUCKLEBERRY: Pap can tell easy. He says when they keep looking at you right steady, they're witching you. 'Specially if they mumble, because when they mumble, they're saying the Lord's Prayer backwards.

TOM: Say, Hucky, when are you going to try the cat?

HUCKLEBERRY: Tonight. They just buried old Hoss

Williams on Saturday. I reckon the devils will come after him tonight.

Tom: Why didn't they get him on Saturday night?

Huckleberry: How you talk! How could their charms work till midnight? Then it was Sunday. Devils don't slosh around much of a Sunday.

Tom: I never thought of that. That's so. Say, Huck, let me go with you.

Huckleberry: Sure, if you're not afraid. I'll come around to your house tonight.

Tom: Will you meow?

Huckleberry: Yes—and you meow back if you get a chance. Last time you kept me meowing till old Mr. Hays went to throwing rocks at me and saying "Dern that cat!" I hove a brick through his window, but don't you tell.

Tom: I won't. I couldn't meow that night because Aunt Polly was watching me, but I'll meow this time.

Huckleberry: We better give the sign once, just to be sure.

Tom: Meow!

Huckleberry: Meow!

Both (*In unison*): Meee-oooww!

Music: *Adventurous theme, in and under. Out.*

Huckleberry (*In close, in a whisper, as throughout the scene*): I reckon this is the part of the graveyard we want.

Tom: Hucky, do you believe the dead people like for us to be here?

Huckleberry: I wish I knew. It's awfully solemn, isn't it?

Tom: I'll bet it is! Say, Huck, do you reckon Hoss Williams hears us talking?

HUCKLEBERRY: Of course he does. Leastwise his spirit does. A body can't be too particular how he talks about these dead people, Tom.

TOM: Sh-h-h!

HUCKLEBERRY: What is it?

TOM: Sh-h-h! There 'tis again! Don't you hear it?

HUCKLEBERRY: I—

TOM: There! Now you hear it!

HUCKLEBERRY: Lord, Tom, they're coming! The devils are coming, sure. What'll we do?

TOM: I don't know. Think they'll see us? They can see in the dark, same as cats. I wish I hadn't come.

HUCKLEBERRY: I'm all a-shiver! Look, three of 'em. It's the devils, sure enough. Tom, can you pray?

SOUND: *Jumbled voices of three men, unintelligible, in background, fading on.*

TOM: I'll try, but don't you be afraid. They aren't going to hurt us. Now I lay me down to sleep, I pray—

HUCKLEBERRY: Sh-h-h.

TOM: What is it, Huck?

HUCKLEBERRY: They're *humans!* One of 'em is, anyway. I recognize old Muff Potter's voice.

TOM: I reckon you're right. Stick close to these elm trees, and he'll never see us. He's too slow. They're looking for Hoss Williams' grave. They're pointed right at it! Say, Huck, I know another of those voices. It's Injun Joe!

HUCKLEBERRY: That's so—that murdering thief! I'd rather they were devils by a long shot. What can they be up to?

TOM: Hush! The other one is young Doc Robinson. I know! They're grave robbers! We'd better be quiet, Hucky, and listen!

ROBINSON (*Off mike, as are the other men throughout the scene*): Here it is, this is the grave. Hurry, men. The moon might come out at any moment.

MUFF: Ah, take your time, Dr. Robinson, take your time.

ROBINSON: That's it, Potter. Dig, dig. Here, let me give you a hand, Injun Joe.

INJUN JOE: There it is. There is the coffin.

MUFF: Now the thing's ready, Sawbones, and you'll just have to give us another five, or we'll leave it here.

INJUN JOE: That's the talk, Muff.

ROBINSON: Look here, what does this mean? You required your pay in advance, and I've paid you.

INJUN JOE: Yes, and you did more than that. Five years ago you drove me away from your father's kitchen one night, Dr. Robinson, when I came to ask for something to eat. You said I wasn't there for any good.

ROBINSON (*A bit afraid*): Now, now, Injun Joe.

INJUN JOE: When I swore I'd get even with you if it took a hundred years, your father had me jailed for a vagrant. Did you think I'd forget? Oh, no, you aren't counting on old Injun Joe.

MUFF: You tell the old Sawbones, Joe.

INJUN JOE: So now I have you, and you have to settle.

ROBINSON: Why, you thieving blackguard! There!

MUFF: Here, now, don't you hit my pard!

SOUND: *Men fighting, through following speeches.*

MEN (*Ad lib*): There! That's it, Joe! Give it to him good. (*Etc.*)

TOM (*Whispering*): Golly, Huck, it's a real fight!

HUCKLEBERRY: What's going on, Tom? I can't see.

TOM: Doc Robinson just hit Muff Potter over the head with a gravestone.

HUCKLEBERRY: Is Muff killed?

TOM: I don't reckon so. Just passed out. Oh! Oh, Huckleberry! Oh!

HUCKLEBERRY: What is it, Tom? What's happened?

TOM: Injun Joe. He—he's stabbed the doctor! With
Muff's knife, too!

HUCKLEBERRY: He'll hang for it, the murderer!

TOM: But look there. He's putting the knife into Muff's
hand. Hush! Muff is coming to. Listen!

MUFF (*Off mike, groaning*): Oh, oh! Why—why, what's
this, Joe?

INJUN JOE: It's a dirty business. What did you kill him
for, Muff?

MUFF: I! I never did it!

INJUN JOE: Look here! That kind of talk won't wash.

MUFF (*Bewildered, sobbing*): I didn't do it, I swear it!
Tell me, Joe—honest, now, old feller—did I do it? Joe,
I never meant to—upon my soul and honor, I never
meant to, Joe. Tell me how it was, Joe. Oh, it's awful—
and him so young and promising.

INJUN JOE: You two were scuffling, and he fetched you one
with the gravestone, and you fell flat; and then up you
came, all reeling and staggering, and snatched the knife
and jammed it into him, just as he fetched you another
awful clip—and here you've laid, as dead as a wedge till
now.

MUFF: I didn't know what I was doing. I wish I may die
this minute if I did. Joe, don't tell. Say you won't tell,
Joe—that's a good feller. I always liked you, Joe, and
stood up for you, too. Don't you remember? You *won't*
tell, *will* you, Joe?

INJUN JOE: No, you've always been fair and square with

me, Muff Potter, and I won't go back on you. There, now, that's as fair as a man can say.

MUFF: Joe, I'll bless you for this the longest day I live.

INJUN JOE: Come now, that's enough of that. This isn't any time for blubbering. You be off yonder way, and I'll go this. Move, now, and don't leave any tracks behind you.

MUFF (*Fading*): Joe, you're my best friend in the world, old feller.

INJUN JOE (*Laughing loudly and hard*): The old fool! He believed me, all right. (*Fading*) That'll settle him, all right. (*Fades, laughing*)

TOM (*Excitedly, but in a whisper, close*): Huckleberry, such awful goings-on. What do you reckon will come of this?

HUCKLEBERRY: I reckon hanging will come of it.

TOM: Do you, though?

HUCKLEBERRY: Why, I *know* it, Tom.

TOM: Who'll tell? We?

HUCKLEBERRY: What are you talking about? Suppose something happened and Injun Joe *didn't* hang? Why, he'd kill us some time or other, just as dead sure as we're lying here.

TOM: That's just what I was thinking to myself, Huck.

HUCKLEBERRY: If anybody tells, let Muff Potter do it, if he's fool enough.

TOM: Muff thinks he did it himself. That's what Injun Joe *made* him think!

HUCKLEBERRY: By hokey, that's so, Tom!

TOM: Hucky, are you sure you can keep mum about this?

HUCKLEBERRY: Tom, we *have* to keep mum. You know that. That Injun devil wouldn't make any more of drowning us than a couple of cats, if we were to squeak about this and they didn't hang him. Now, look here, Tom, let's take an oath and swear to each other—that's what we have to do—swear to keep mum.

TOM: I agree. It's the best thing. Would you just hold hands and swear that we—

HUCKLEBERRY: No, that wouldn't do for this. That's good enough for little rubbishy common things, 'specially with gals, because *they* go back on you anyway, and blab if they get in a huff, but there should be writing about a big thing like this. And blood!

TOM: I reckon you're right, Hucky. I have a pencil here —but what can we write on?

HUCKLEBERRY: How about this piece of bark? It's smooth.

TOM: Say, that's a whack. Now let me write it down. (*Reading, as he writes*) "Huck Finn—and Tom Sawyer —swear they will keep mum—about this—and they wish —they may drop down dead—in their tracks—if they ever tell—and rot."

HUCKLEBERRY: Say, that's grand, Tom. Here, I have a pin to draw blood with.

TOM: Hold on! Don't do that! A pin's brass—that's poison. I have a needle. I'll just prick my finger—ow! There! Now, I'll sign my initials—T and S.

HUCKLEBERRY: Let me do mine, Tom. Ow! But, Tom, I can't write. How do I make my initials?

TOM: I'll guide your hand along. H—and—F. There!

HUCKLEBERRY: Tom, does this keep us from *ever* telling— *always?*

TOM: Of course it does. It doesn't make any difference *what* happens, we have to keep mum. We'd drop down dead—don't you know that?

HUCKLEBERRY: Yes, I reckon that's so. Oh, Tom, Tom, I'm scared. What'll happen if—if you-know-who finds out we were here tonight?

TOM: Huckleberry, if that ever happens, well—I reckon I'd rather not think about it.

MUSIC: *Adventurous theme, in and under. Out.*

TOM: Morning, Aunt Polly.

AUNT POLLY (*A robust, matronly voice*): Morning, Tom. You sleep well last night?

TOM: I reckon so, auntie.

AUNT POLLY: I'm glad to hear *some* people can still have a good night in this town, but I don't know how long it'll last. Tom, young Dr. Robinson was killed in the graveyard last night.

TOM (*Nervously*): Wh—who did it?

AUNT POLLY: Muff Potter!

TOM: Oh, no he didn't—I mean, well, how do they know?

AUNT POLLY: They found his knife at the scene of the crime. But what did you mean, "he didn't"?

TOM: Why, er—nothing, aunt. Nothing at all. Honest!

AUNT POLLY: I'm going down to the graveyard to see the bloodstains. Everybody in town will be there, I reckon. Maybe there'll be some news of whether they've caught that Potter yet. Want to come, Tom? (*Fading*) That Muff Potter should be ridden out of town on a rail, he should!

MUSIC: *Adventurous theme, in and under. Out.*

SOUND: *Murmuring of the crowd of townspeople.*

TOWNSPEOPLE (*Ad lib*): What an awful deed! Poor young fellow, Robinson. Curse that Muff Potter. (*Etc.*)

AUNT POLLY: Did you ever hear of such a brutal thing in your life?

1st WOMAN: I never did. No, no, I never did.

1st MAN: I always said that Potter was a bad one.

AUNT POLLY: Have they caught him yet?

1st WOMAN: Not yet. No one's seen hide nor hair of him.

2ND WOMAN: They're sure he did it. Why, there's no doubt about it. They found his knife.

1st MAN: Injun Joe was here when it happened. He swears it was Muff!

SOUND: *The crowd becomes agitated.*

TOWNSPEOPLE (*Ad lib*): Look, it's him! He's come back to the scene of his crime! Catch him! It's Muff Potter. (*Etc.*)

AUNT POLLY: What's all the excitement over there?

2ND WOMAN: Why, look! It's Muff Potter!

2ND MAN (*Off mike*): I have you now, Potter. You won't get away!

MUFF (*Fading on, sobbing*): I didn't do it, friends. Upon my word, I didn't!

1st MAN (*In derision*): Who's accused you?

1st WOMAN: Talk to Injun Joe, over there, about that!

MUFF: Injun Joe, you promised me you'd never—

2ND MAN: Is that your knife?

MUFF: Tell 'em, Joe. Tell 'em—it's no use any more. They have me. Tell 'em the truth, Joe.

INJUN JOE: Yes, he did it. Just like I said in court, this morning. Muff Potter killed Doc Robinson with that knife that the Sheriff's holding. Killed him in cold blood, I say! He ought to hang!

TOM (*In a frightened whisper*): Oh, Hucky, hear the liar! What'll we do?

HUCKLEBERRY (*Whispering*): We swore to keep mum, Tom. Remember?

AUNT POLLY (*In an angry whisper*): Stop your talking, boys. I can't hear a word they're saying.

2ND WOMAN: Why didn't you leave, Potter? Why'd you come back here? To look at your handiwork?

MUFF: I couldn't help it—I couldn't help it. I tried to run away, but—oh, it's no use. Take me away, Sheriff. Take me away.

MUSIC: *Sad theme, in and under. Out.*

AUNT POLLY: Thomas Sawyer, it's about time you got up. You've been abed half the morning. What ails you, boy?

TOM: I—I didn't sleep very well, Aunt Polly.

AUNT POLLY: I reckon I know that. I heard you tossing and turning all night. What do you have on your mind, boy?

TOM: Nothing! I don't—I don't have anything on my mind, aunt. Honest!

AUNT POLLY: I can't understand you. You're acting so jittery all of a sudden. And moaning words in your sleep!

TOM (*Frightened*): What did I say? Did you hear me say anything?

AUNT POLLY: You kept saying "Blood! It's blood—that's what it is!" over and over. And you said "Don't torment me so—I'll tell!" Tell *what?* What is it you'll tell?

TOM: I—I—aunt, don't ask me any questions.

AUNT POLLY (*Pleasantly*): I know what it is. You've been thinking about that awful murder. I reckon all of us have. That's what has you so upset. Well, don't worry, Tom. Muff Potter will hang for it, sure enough. Now you go out and play.

TOM (*Beginning to fade*): Yes, aunt.

AUNT POLLY: After he hangs, you won't have a thing to worry about.

TOM (*Continuing to fade off*): Oh, no, aunt! That's when my worries will just begin!

MUSIC: *Mock-serious theme, in and under. Out.*

HUCKLEBERRY: Morning, Tom.

TOM: Morning, Huck. Say—say, Hucky. Have you ever told anybody about—about *that?*

HUCKLEBERRY: Of course I haven't. Never a solitary word, so help me. What makes you ask?

TOM: Well, I was afraid.

HUCKLEBERRY: Why, Tom Sawyer, we wouldn't be alive two days if I told. You know that.

TOM (*Slowly*): Yes, but—but—

HUCKLEBERRY: But what? Tom Sawyer, nobody could get *you* to tell, could they?

TOM: No, Hucky. Of course not. Only I've been hearing a powerful lot of talk around lately.

HUCKLEBERRY: What talk?

TOM: Everywhere I go, it's just Muff Potter, Muff Potter, Muff Potter all the time.

HUCKLEBERRY: That's just the same way they go on around me. I reckon he's a goner.

TOM: Don't you feel sorry for him sometimes?

HUCK: Most always. He's no account; but then he hasn't ever done anything to hurt anybody. He's kind of good. He gave me half a fish, once, when there wasn't enough for two; and lots of times he's stood by me when I was out of luck.

TOM: Well, he's mended kites for me, Huck, and knitted hooks onto my line. I wish we could get him out of there.

HUCK: We couldn't do that. But say! We could go down

to see him, and talk to him, and maybe bring him some things.

TOM: I think he'd like that a lot, Hucky. You see what you can fetch up, and I'll do the same. I'll meet you at the jailhouse window. Right, Huckleberry?

HUCKLEBERRY: Right, Tom.

MUSIC: *Light theme, in and under. Out.*

MUFF: It sure was good of you boys to come down and bring me this stuff. You've been mighty good to me, boys—better than anybody else in this town. I don't forget, I don't. Often I say to myself, "I used to mend all the boys' kites and things, and show 'em where the good fishing places were, and befriend 'em all I could, and now they've all forgotten old Muff Potter when he's in trouble. But Tom doesn't and Huck doesn't—*they* don't forget him," I say, "and I don't forget them." Stand over to the light, boys, that's it. It's a prime comfort to see faces that are friendly when a body's in such a muck of trouble, and none come here but you. Good, friendly faces—good, friendly faces. Shake hands with me, boys. Yours'll come through the bars, but mine's too big. Little hands and weak—but they've helped Muff Potter a powerful lot, and I know they'd help him more if they could.

MUSIC: *Melancholy theme, sneak in under.*

TOM (*Without a pause, over the music, tearfully*): Huck —oh, Huck—we just have to tell. We just have to.

HUCKLEBERRY: You want to drop down dead, Tom Sawyer? Remember what we wrote in blood?

TOM (*Sadly*): I reckon you're right, Huckleberry. I—I reckon you're right.

MUSIC: *Melancholy theme full, then under. Out.*

SOUND: *Indoor clock striking ten.*

AUNT POLLY: Hm-m. Ten o'clock. I wonder if Tom is asleep yet. Mercy, the way that boy has been fussing in his bed these past few nights! What with the trial of Muff Potter set for tomorrow, I'll warrant he's having a bad time of it. I'll just go up and see how he is, and maybe tuck in his covers a bit—poor boy! Poor, worried boy!

MUSIC: *Quiet theme, in briefly, then under. Out.*

AUNT POLLY (*Off mike softly*): Tom, Tom, you asleep?

TOM (*On mike; groaning and mumbling in his sleep*): Oh-h! Oh-h! Blood! No, he didn't do it.

AUNT POLLY (*In amazement*): What's this?

TOM: I'll tell. It wasn't Muff Potter. He didn't do it. Ask —ask Huckleberry. It was Injun Joe!

AUNT POLLY: Injun Joe!

TOM: We saw it. Oh! Huck's dead cat—graveyard. It wasn't Muff Potter that did it. It was—it was Injun Joe. Swore not to tell, but—got to—got to save Muff Potter from hanging.

AUNT POLLY: So that's why the boy's been so upset. He saw the whole thing. And it was Injun Joe! (*Fading*) I'm going to see the Sheriff—right away!

MUSIC: *Adventurous theme, in and under. Out.*

SOUND: *Murmur of townspeople in court; pounding of a gavel.*

JUDGE: Silence! We will proceed with this trial in quiet! Order, or I'll clear the court.

SOUND: *The murmuring subsides.*

JUDGE: Counsel for the prosecution, will you make your statement?

PROSECUTION: Yes, Your Honor. By the oaths of citizens whose simple word is above suspicion, we have fastened this awful crime, beyond all possibility of question, upon Muff Potter, the unhappy prisoner at the bar. We rest our case.

MUFF: No, no!

DEFENSE: Your Honor, may I call one final witness?

JUDGE: You may. Who is it?

DEFENSE: Call Thomas Sawyer!

TOWNSPEOPLE (*Ad lib*): Tom Sawyer! Why him? (*Etc.*)

HUCKLEBERRY: Tom! You said you wouldn't!

TOM: I didn't, Huck. I didn't!

JUDGE: Thomas Sawyer, place your hand on the Bible. Do you swear to tell the truth, the whole truth, and nothing but the truth, so help you God?

TOM: I—I guess so, Judge.

DEFENSE: Thomas Sawyer, where were you on the night of the seventeenth of June, at the hour of midnight?

TOM: In the graveyard, sir.

DEFENSE: You may speak louder. Don't be afraid. Were you anywhere near Horse Williams' grave?

TOM: Yes, sir. Near as I am to you. I was hidden behind the elm trees on the edge of the grave.

DEFENSE: Anyone with you?

TOM: Yes, sir. I went there with Huckleberry Finn. We had his dead cat with us.

SOUND: *Laughter in background.*

DEFENSE: We will produce the skeleton of that cat later. Now, my boy, tell us everything that occurred—tell it in your own way. Don't skip anything, and don't be afraid.

TOM: Well, sir, Huck and I saw the three of them come to

the grave. Then Injun Joe asked the Doc for more money. The Doc said no. So they started fighting. Doc Robinson knocked Muff Potter out with a headstone. Injun Joe jumped up with Muff's knife in his hand, and he—

SOUND: *Crash of wood, then of glass. Commotion in the court.*

TOWNSPEOPLE: (*Ad lib*): It's Injun Joe! He's escaping! Out the window! Catch him! After him! (*Etc.*)

MUSIC: *Adventurous theme, in and under. Out.*

AUNT POLLY: I'm proud of you, Tom. You did a grand thing in court today.

JUDGE: That you did, son.

TOM: Thank you, Aunt Polly. Thanks a lot, Judge. But if it hadn't been for Huckleberry Finn, we wouldn't have been able to save Muff Potter at all.

AUNT POLLY: We are all grateful to you, too, Huckleberry.

HUCKLEBERRY: Thank you, ma'am. But could I say somethin' to Tom? Alone, I mean?

AUNT POLLY: Why certainly. I understand you boys. You *will* have your secrets. Come along, Judge. I've some tea on the stove.

JUDGE (*Fading*): Fine, fine. We can discuss the reward the boys are to get, now that Injun Joe is captured and Muff set free.

TOM: Did you hear that, Huck? We're going to get a reward!

HUCKLEBERRY (*Sadly*): What good will a reward be, if we're both going to drop down dead for telling?

TOM: Well, seeing as how I didn't get a chance to *really* tell—

HUCKLEBERRY: How's that?

Том: It was Aunt Polly. She heard me talking in my sleep. When it was *my* turn, in court, Injun Joe escaped before the tale was finished. So I reckon we're not going to drop dead after all.

Huckleberry: Why, that's *bully,* Tom!

Том: You can bet it is, Huckleberry. Isn't it grand, being heroes?

Aunt Polly (*Fading on, angrily*): Tom Sawyer! I just went to the cream pitcher to serve the Judge with his tea, and there wasn't any left. *Somebody* was there before me, and *drank* it all. I can tell you you're in for a licking, young man!

Huckleberry (*Apprehensively*): Looks like we're through with being heroes, Tom.

Том (*Resignedly*): That's the way it is, Huckleberry. A fellow just can't win—no, not ever!

Music: *Lighthearted theme, full to finish.*

THE END

The Crowning of King Arthur

The Crowning of King Arthur

From *Morte d'Arthur* by Sir Thomas Malory

Characters

SIR BRASTIAS	GUINEVERE
MERLIN	THREE MEN
SIR ECTOR	TWO WOMEN
SIR LIONEL	TWO KNIGHTS
SIR KAY	NARRATOR
ARTHUR	

NARRATOR: One of the greatest legends of all time is that of England's King Arthur and his Knights of the Round Table. For centuries, minstrels have been singing his story and troubadors telling his tale. Of all the many versions of this fabulous romance, none is as deeply respected and as dearly loved as *Morte d'Arthur,* by Sir Thomas Malory, completed in the year 1470. Malory's epic retelling of the Arthurian legends has formed the basis for novels, plays, and operas the world over. It is a long romance, as richly detailed as a Gothic stained-glass window, as colorful as a medieval tapestry. Here is one episode from it: the story of how Arthur became king, from *The Death of Arthur—Morte d'Arthur—*by Sir Thomas Malory.

SOUND: *Tolling of bells, with crowd noises in background.*

1ST MAN (*Fading on*): What is the news? Why do the bells toll in such alarm?

1ST WOMAN (*Fading on*): What calamity calls us to the church in such disorder?

2ND MAN: What evil tidings are afoot?

3RD MAN (*Off mike*): Have you heard the news?

1ST MAN: No, no. Tell us at once!

3RD MAN (*Fading on*): King Uther is dead!

1ST WOMAN (*In anguish*): Woe! Alas!

2ND WOMAN (*Unable to believe*): What? The King?

3RD MAN: But two weeks gone, he fell sick of a great malady, and today he died thereof.

2ND MAN: And who is to take the throne in his place?

3RD MAN: No one knows.

2ND WOMAN: Are we to have no king?

3RD MAN: They say that many knights are claiming the honor for themselves. No two agree on who is rightly king.

1ST WOMAN: Alack the day! Our realm stands in great danger. Who knows what evil will result from this untimely death of good King Uther?

2ND WOMAN: I fear me you are right. Evil days indeed lie before us.

2ND MAN: Before us—and before our England.

MUSIC: *Dramatic theme, up full and out.*

NARRATOR: Evil days did indeed come to England. King Uther was dead, leaving behind no man whom all would accept as a new king. On every hand stood knights and lords and princes, eager for the throne. Each was ready to defend his claim, but none was prepared to lend support to the claim of another. As petty skirmishing between knights broke out, the situation became more threatening. Both the nobility and the general population dreaded the bloodshed and destruction that might follow if things were allowed to run their course. And so, at last, the nobles turned to Merlin, a wise and powerful magician who had been the late king's trusted friend, and asked him for advice.

SIR BRASTIAS: This controversy over who is to be king must be put to an end, Merlin. Someone must be named to succeed our late lord.

MERLIN: Indeed, Sir Brastias, you speak truly.

SIR ECTOR: But how can we know which man is the true king? Uther left no son. We cannot let the crown fall to any man not destined by heaven for the throne.

SIR BRASTIAS: I fear you are right, Sir Ector. It is a difficult matter.

SIR ECTOR: What say you, Merlin? You were the late king's friend and advisor. All are agreed that in such matters yours is the wisdom that can prevail.

MERLIN: You do me too much honor, Sir Ector. I cannot decide who is to be king.

SIR BRASTIAS: If you cannot, who can?

MERLIN: Heaven must decide, for when men have not wisdom themselves, only heaven can provide an answer.

SIR ECTOR: What do you propose?

MERLIN: Let every nobleman of the realm come together with his peers before the church in London on Christmas morn. There we shall see if it will be made known to us who is rightly and truly king.

SIR BRASTIAS: You look for a miracle, do you, Merlin?

MERLIN: I do. And if it be God's will, on Christmas morn, we shall have a sign. On Christmas, we shall know our future king.

MUSIC: *Grand theme, up full and out.*

NARRATOR: And so it was agreed. On Christmas morning, even before the sky was light, the yard of London Church was filled with eager nobles, each hoping in his heart that *his* would be the chosen name.

MERLIN: Good Christmas to you all, my lords, and happily met.

SIR BRASTIAS: Good Christmas, indeed, Merlin. But where is the sign from heaven that you promised? Has it come?

MERLIN: I promised no sign, Sir Brastias. I said only that if it were God's will, a miracle might come to pass. Perhaps it is not God's will.

SIR BRASTIAS: Woe betide England if the sign come not soon. The lords are restless, Merlin, and the citizens unhappy. We cannot be without a king forever.

MERLIN: Let every man bow his head in prayer. Look: the sky is growing clear. Day is breaking. Let us pray that in the same fashion, wisdom will come dawning in our hearts.

NARRATOR: And so the assembled lords bowed their heads in prayer. As they prayed, the sky grew lighter, and when they raised their heads, it was full morning.

SIR BRASTIAS (*Excitedly*): Look, Merlin, look!

SIR ECTOR: That stone, standing in the middle of the yard!

SIR LIONEL: I've never seen it there before.

SIR BRASTIAS: What is its meaning, Merlin?

MERLIN: This is the sign for which we have prayed.

SIR LIONEL: What? That great marble slab with an anvil on it? How can that be a sign?

MERLIN: Only look, my friends. Look at the stone closely. Lodged deep in the anvil is a sword.

SIR ECTOR: Why, so there is.

SIR LIONEL: The fairest sword that ever I did see.

MERLIN: And see: About the sword are letters burned in gold.

SIR BRASTIAS: What do they say, Merlin?

MERLIN: "Whoso pulleth out this sword of this stone and anvil, is rightwise King born of all England."

SIR ECTOR: Praise God. It is the sign.

SIR LIONEL: But anyone may pull a sword from a scabbard, even if the scabbard be of steel.

MERLIN: It may not be so simple as it looks, my friend. Now let every man and lord try his skill. Each must have a turn. Pull at the sword, my noble friends. Pull with all your might. It will be to no avail, unless you are the one truly chosen of heaven. For it is a sign from God: whoso pulleth out this sword of this stone and anvil, only he is rightwise King born of all England.

MUSIC: *Dramatic theme, in and under. Out.*

NARRATOR: Thus it was decided that every knight and lord would try his skill at removing the marvelous sword from the steel anvil in the yard of London Church. Knights came from far and near to attempt the deed, but the sword held fast. No matter how hard the knights tried, no matter how much they strained, the sword would not yield. Now the knights became angrier than ever.

SIR BRASTIAS: Merlin, we are no better off with this magic sword than we were before it came. Something must be done.

MERLIN (*Calmly*): There is nothing to be done but wait.

Sooner or later, the true king will put his hand upon the sword. And when he does, the stone and anvil will yield it up to him.

SIR BRASTIAS: And what are we to do in the meantime?

SIR LIONEL: How are we to keep peace among the lords until this true king does come?

SIR BRASTIAS: The quarreling has begun again.

MERLIN: I have a plan. Let there be a tournament.

SIR LIONEL: A tournament?

SIR BRASTIAS: What good will that do?

MERLIN: Listen. Let every knight who would be king. . . .

SIR BRASTIAS (*Interrupting*): And that, I warrant, means *every* knight!

MERLIN: Let them all gather in London Field three days hence for a tournament. Let each knight joust as best he may, until all but one are eliminated.

SIR BRASTIAS: And he that is left as victor shall be named England's king?

MERLIN: It is my hope that before the day comes when only one knight remains in the field, the true king will have come and removed the sword from the stone. But if he has not come, then the victor of the tournament shall be king.

MUSIC: *Active theme, in and under. Out.*

NARRATOR: News of the tournament spread far and wide, and when the appointed day arrived, every knight in Britain was on hand in London Field. Such a splendid sight it was! Each knight was dressed in his most splendid armor, his brightest trappings, his richest plumes. The banners were flying; ribbons were dancing in the breeze. On every hand was a wild display of gorgeous color and fabulous richness. Among the knights who hoped to win the joust was Sir Kay, eldest son of the noble Sir Ector, who sought his father's blessing before the combat.

SIR KAY: Do you wish me Godspeed in today's tourney, Father?

SIR ECTOR: That I do with all my heart, Kay. And if it be God's will that you sit upon the throne of England, may you bear yourself as valiantly as a king as you have always done as a son.

SIR KAY: My lord, I thank you with all my heart.

SIR ECTOR: Here, Kay, is a scarf of your mother's. Tie it about your arm as you enter the lists, and think of her memory as you prepare to joust. It grieves my heart that she cannot see how fine you look at this hour.

SIR KAY: Do I please you, Father?

SIR ECTOR: I warrant there is none finer. But where is your younger brother? He should be here to see you in your splendor. (*Calling out*) Arthur! Arthur! Where is that lad, I wonder? Arthur!

ARTHUR (*Fading on*): Did you call me, Father?

SIR ECTOR: Aye, Arthur. Why are you not by your brother's side, helping him to make ready for the tourney?

ARTHUR (*Earnestly*): Oh, do forgive me, Kay, my dearest brother.

SIR KAY: Do not be alarmed, Arthur. I am not angry.

ARTHUR (*Excitedly*): Oh, Father, how splendid it all is. How I wish that I were a knight, that I might enter the lists today.

SIR ECTOR (*Kindly*): All in good time, Arthur, my son. You are still but a lad. Today we must watch your brother. Your turn will come within a few years, but today you must help Kay.

ARTHUR: With all my heart, Father. Kay knows how much I wish him Godspeed.

SIR KAY: I do, indeed, Arthur.

SOUND: *Fanfare.*

SIR ECTOR: Come, my son. It is time to take up your sword. Mount your horse, and Arthur will hand the weapon up to you.

SIR KAY: Aye, Father. But—that is strange. Where *is* my sword?

ARTHUR: Is it not with your helmet?

SIR ECTOR: What have you done with it?

SIR KAY (*Sheepishly*): I fear I have left it at our lodgings, Father.

SIR ECTOR: Arthur. Here is your chance to do some fancy riding today, although it be not in the lists. Take my horse, and get you back to our lodgings as fast as you are able. Fetch your brother's sword, and bring it here at once.

ARTHUR (*Happily*): That will I do with the greatest pleasure. Fear not, brother Kay. I will fetch your sword for you. (*Fading*) Just see if I do not come in half the time you think!

SIR ECTOR (*Contemplatively*): He's a fine lad, is Arthur, and will, one day, become as fine a man as any in the kingdom. I love him as though he were my own flesh and blood.

SIR KAY: Does Arthur know that he is not truly your son and my brother, Father? Have you ever told him?

SIR ECTOR: That I never have, nor does the boy even suspect as much. I have always regarded him as dearly as I have you. What difference does it make if he is not of our blood? If I may have my way, that is something that Arthur never shall know.

MUSIC: *Dramatic theme, in and under. Out.*

NARRATOR: While Sir Ector and his son, Sir Kay, stood discussing the young lad, Arthur himself was off by horse for the family's lodgings. Within a few minutes, the young boy had reached London Square. And there he had a sudden thought.

ARTHUR: Why should I waste time by going all the way to our lodgings to fetch a sword for Kay, when I have heard that in the yard of London Church there stands a sword in an anvil, just waiting for someone to take it. Why should I not take *that* sword? I could be back to the tourney in no time. Surely it could not be considered stealing, for I have heard tell that every man who passes by is *encouraged* to take it. I—I believe I will!

NARRATOR: Lightly Arthur dropped from the saddle, and ran to the yard of the church. There, just as he had been told, stood the slab of marble with the steel anvil; and deeply imbedded in the anvil was the sword.

ARTHUR: There is writing above the sword, but I dare not take the time to read it. Every minute that I stand here is a minute lost for my brother, Sir Kay. I'll just take the sword, and if the writing be of interest, no doubt my father will tell me of it when I see him.

NARRATOR: With that, Arthur stretched out his hand, grasped the handle of the sword, and pulled it from the anvil as easily as if it had been a pocketknife wedged in the rind of an orange. Mounting his horse once again, he turned and headed back for London Field.

ARTHUR: Here is a sword, brother Kay. Though it be not

your own, I warrant it is a good sword and true, and will serve you well in the jousts to come.

SIR KAY (*Taken aback*): How—how came you by this sword, Arthur?

ARTHUR: Never fear, Kay. I did not steal it.

SIR ECTOR (*Fading on*): What's this, Arthur? Back so soon with the sword? You have done a good day's riding, my son, and as you promised, are returned in half the time I looked for.

SIR KAY (*Nervously*): Father, look you at this sword I hold. It is the sword from the stone, Father.

SIR ECTOR: How came you by this sword, my son? Answer me truthfully, for you will be too easily discovered if you say aught but what is true in this matter.

SIR KAY: Sir, by my brother Arthur, for he brought it to me.

ARTHUR: I meant no harm by it, Father. Are you angry?

SIR ECTOR: How got you this sword, Arthur? Speak truly.

ARTHUR: Sir, I will tell you. When I went home for my brother's sword, I saw this one standing in a stone in the yard of London Church. Wishing to return to the joust as quickly as possible, I thought my brother Kay should have this sword to use, and so I pulled it from the anvil without any pain.

SIR ECTOR: My son, my son.

ARTHUR (*Amazed*): Father, why do you kneel before me?

SIR ECTOR: For I understand that you must be king of this land.

ARTHUR: I? Wherefore I?

SIR ECTOR: Never should man have drawn out this sword from the rock but that he shall be rightwise king of this land. Did you not read the legend burned in gold about the stone?

ARTHUR: No, my lord. I did not wish to waste the time. Mine own dear father and brother, do you mock me? Why do you kneel?

SIR ECTOR: Nay, Arthur, it is not so. I was never your father nor of your blood.

ARTHUR: Surely, my lord, you speak in riddles. You are my own dear father.

SIR ECTOR: It is not so. Listen and I will tell you. Many years ago, an old man brought to my home a baby newly born, and gave him into my charge. I raised that babe as though he were my own, never knowing of what family he rightly came, and never caring. You were that child, Arthur. Now I know well you are of a higher blood than I thought. Will you be my good and gracious lord when you are king?

ARTHUR: Sir, never in my life could I hold you in less than highest esteem. To you I owe more than I can ever repay; and if it be God's will that I be king, whatever you may desire of me, that shall I do. Both for you and yours will I be ready; and if you ask it, were I king of a thousand Englands, I would lay down my life for you.

SIR ECTOR: You have spoken well, Arthur. Come; we must tell the assembled lords of what you have done. We must hail the new king. Long live King Arthur!

MUSIC: *Dramatic theme, up full and out.*

NARRATOR: At last the truth was known. The boy, Arthur, adopted in infancy by Sir Ector, and raised as his own son, was in truth the child of King Uther, and rightful heir to the throne of England. Still a boy, Arthur was spurned by many of the lords, who refused to recognize him as their sovereign, hoping against hope that a mistake had been made, and that one of *them* would be chosen to rule.

1ST KNIGHT (*Angrily*): He's but a boy! Who is he to rule all England?

MERLIN: But did he not pull the sword from the anvil? None of you was able to do it.

2ND KNIGHT: Perhaps it was a trick. Perhaps he used magic.

1ST KNIGHT: You're a magician yourself, Merlin. Perhaps you helped the boy to do it.

MERLIN: It was no magic, no trick. Let the boy be tested again. Let each of the knights have another trial at the sword. You will see: only Arthur will be able to pull it from the anvil.

1ST KNIGHT: Let us postpone the coronation until Candlemas. Perhaps another knight will come—one who has not yet tried his skill.

MERLIN: As you desire it, so let it be. But I can promise you that none will come to pull the sword from the stone. As Arthur did at Christmas, so will he do at Candlemas. As he does at Candlemas, so will he do at Easter, and so will he do at the Feast of Pentecost. It is not meet that you should put off accepting him as your liege. There is but one true King of England, and that is the boy Arthur.

MUSIC: *Royal theme, up and out.*

NARRATOR: As Merlin had predicted, the results of the trial of the sword and anvil were the same at Candlemas as they had been at Christmas. All the knights of the realm tried to pull the sword from its magic scabbard, but none succeeded, except for Arthur. At last, the people grew tired of postponements. And though the knights had kept Arthur from his throne, the people of London were determined to seat him there.

SOUND: *Noise of a large crowd in background.*

1ST MAN: Give us Arthur for our king!

2ND MAN: Let us put him no more in delay!

1ST WOMAN: Everyone can see it is God's will that he be king!

2ND WOMAN: As God wishes, so also do we. Give us Arthur!

3RD MAN: And let him that holdeth against the king look to himself, for we will slay him.

2ND WOMAN: Long live the king!

1ST MAN: Long live the king!

ALL (*Shouting*): The king is dead. Long live the king. Long live King Arthur!

MUSIC: *Dramatic theme, up full and out.*

NARRATOR: At last the kingdom was agreed. The young Arthur was to be crowned. As the day of coronation drew closer, Arthur sent for Merlin to ask his advice.

ARTHUR: Merlin, I am well aware that you were chief counselor to my father, the late King Uther. I would have you serve me in the selfsame stead.

MERLIN: As you wish it, sire, so shall I do.

ARTHUR: First, then, you must tell me what you think of a plan I have. You know how much love I bear toward Sir Ector, who raised me from a child. Is it meet, think you, that I appoint his son, Sir Kay, as seneschal of all my lands?

MERLIN: Most meet and fitting, sire. It pleases my heart to

see the new king is a good king and a kind man who does not forget his debts. But there is something else that troubles you, I think. Is there not?

ARTHUR: There is, indeed. My barons desire that I marry. But I will not choose a queen, save by thy counsel.

MERLIN: Is there not one already chosen in your heart?

ARTHUR (*Slowly*): Aye, there is one. But I would not have her if you do not think it well.

MERLIN: What lady is it who has won your heart?

ARTHUR: I love Guinevere, daughter of King Leodegrance of Cameliard. She is the fairest and most gentle damsel that ever I have known.

MERLIN: Thou hast chosen wisely, Arthur. King Leodegrance was an old friend of your father. And Guinevere is, in truth, all that you claim, and more. It is meet that she be your wedded wife and your crowned queen.

ARTHUR (*Suddenly*): Oh, Merlin, it is a frightful thing to be chosen England's king.

MERLIN: Frightful, my lord?

ARTHUR: Sometimes, as I lie in bed at night, I cannot sleep. Will I be a good king, I wonder. Will I have wisdom and strength? Will I be honorable and noble, fair and just?

MERLIN: And what answers have you found for these questions, sire?

ARTHUR: Only one answer, Merlin: I shall try. And with the Lady Guinevere at my side, I think—I *hope*—I shall succeed.

MUSIC: *Noble theme, up full and out.*

NARRATOR: When the populace of England learned of Arthur's choice for a bride, there was general rejoicing. For Guinevere was the fairest, gentlest, and noblest lady

England had ever known. With the greatest of pomp and ceremony, the entire royal court, with Arthur at its head, welcomed the bride.

SOUND: *Flourish of trumpets.*

ARTHUR: Welcome to London, fair lady.

GUINEVERE: I thank you, my lord, with all my heart, for the welcome, and for the honor which you have done me in choosing me to be your wife.

ARTHUR: Is it only for the honor that you have come, Guinevere?

GUINEVERE: I do not understand you, my lord. You are the king, and you have sent for me. Is that not reason enough for my coming?

ARTHUR: No, Guinevere. For me that is no reason. I have sent for you because I love you. I had hoped that you would come for the same reason.

GUINEVERE: My lord, I do not mean offense.

ARTHUR: You blush, my lady?

GUINEVERE: With pleasure, sire, at hearing your words. They are sweet to me.

ARTHUR: And have you no words for me? No sweet words?

GUINEVERE: I am a woman, sire, and not used to speaking with men. But I can tell you that my heart is glad and proud at this moment.

ARTHUR: Because you are to be England's queen?

GUINEVERE: No, sire. Of that I am a little afraid. I am glad because . . .

ARTHUR: Because . . .

GUINEVERE: Because I am to be Arthur's wife.

MUSIC: *Romantic theme, in and under. Out.*

NARRATOR: In the days that followed, Arthur and Guinevere spent many hours together, planning the future—

both their own and their country's—and falling ever more deeply in love.

ARTHUR: What would you like for a wedding gift, my love? Is there not something splendid and wonderful that you have dreamed of, longed for?

GUINEVERE (*Contentedly*): No, Arthur, nothing that I do not already have.

ARTHUR: But I want to *give* you something, something more marvelous than you have ever had.

GUINEVERE: You have already done that. You have given me a gift so rich, so wonderful, that all my life I shall try to be worthy of it.

ARTHUR: You speak of the crown?

GUINEVERE: I speak of your love.

ARTHUR: That will I give you over and over and over again, more each day.

GUINEVERE: Being rich in that, I shall want for nothing more. But as we speak of wedding gifts, I have already chosen one for you.

ARTHUR: You are going to give me something, Guinevere?

GUINEVERE: Not give it, really. It would be more right to say that I return it, for it is something that belongs to you by right.

ARTHUR (*Laughing lightly*): You speak in riddles.

GUINEVERE: As you know, our fathers—yours and mine— were great friends.

ARTHUR: Yes, I have often heard of the love between King Uther and King Leodegrance.

GUINEVERE: Many years ago, King Uther sent my father a priceless gift. It is a great round table, richly carved and beautiful beyond imagining. It is large enough to seat one hundred and fifty. It is that I wish to give, for it is rightly yours: the Table Round.

ARTHUR: The Table Round. I thank you, Guinevere, for your gift. I shall treasure it always, because it was once my father's, and because it comes from you. When I am crowned king, I shall have many fine and rich possessions, I have no doubt. But I swear to you that none will ever mean to me what your gift will.

GUINEVERE: You say that so strangely, Arthur. What are you thinking?

ARTHUR: I have just had an idea, my love. The Table Round shall become the center of my court. At it shall sit only the most noble, most virtuous, most brave knights of my kingdom. It shall be the purpose of those who sit at the Table Round to administer justice, and to champion the cause of the weak, the poor, and the innocent. You shall sit at its head, and be its guiding star. Your goodness and virtue, your nobility and gentleness, shall be its hallmarks and its greatest adornment. And we shall all strive to follow the example you set for us, yea, I and all my knights. Together, Guinevere, we shall bring a new dawn to England's civilization. I see it all before me as I speak of it. Ours shall be a happy land, with peace and justice on every side. I told Merlin once that I was afraid of being king. I am afraid no longer. I feel within me the power to do great things. You and I, my love, shall rule as kings have never ruled before. And some day, if God be on our side, men will remember the wonder, the splendor, the glory of Queen Guinevere, King Arthur, and his Knights of the Table Round.

MUSIC: *Prolonged fanfare, followed without break by royal theme, in and under. Out.*

NARRATOR: And so it was that the boy Arthur became King of England, and Guinevere became his queen. As Arthur had prophesied, the Table Round did become the cornerstone of his glorious reign. But the marriage and coronation of Arthur and Guinevere were only the beginning of a long series of adventures. Before their lives were ended, Arthur and Guinevere became involved with a host of legendary figures: Morgan le Fay; Tristram and the fair Isolt; Sir Lancelot of the Lake; the malevolent Sir Modred; the noble Sir Galahad; Sir Pellinore and Sir Percival; Elaine of Astolat; the Lady of the Lake; and many, many more. All of these adventures that form a part of the Arthurian legend, though they are centuries old, are always new, waiting to be discovered again by new readers of Sir Thomas Malory's immortal classic, *Morte d'Arthur.*

MUSIC: *Full to finish.*

THE END